THE STRUCTURE AND
LIFE OF BRYOPHYTES

Biological Sciences

Editor

PROFESSOR A. J. CAIN
MA, D.PHIL
Professor of Zoology in the University of Manchester

THE STRUCTURE AND
LIFE OF BRYOPHYTES

E. V. Watson
Lecturer in Botany in the University of Reading

HUTCHINSON UNIVERSITY LIBRARY
LONDON

HUTCHINSON & CO (*Publishers*) LTD
178–202 Great Portland Street, London W1

London Melbourne Sydney
Auckland Bombay Toronto
Johannesburg New York

First published 1964
Second edition 1967
Reprinted 1968

98479

*This book has been set in Times, printed in Great Britain
on Smooth Wove paper by Anchor Press, and
bound by Wm. Brendon, both of Tiptree, Essex*

09 069783 9   (Cased)
09 069784 7   (Paper)

588
Wat

Contents

Acknowledgments

I should like to thank the following for permission to make use of copyright material: Dr D. J. Carr and the *Australian Journal of Botany* for Fig. 3A; Professor S. Hattori for Figs. 3B and C; Professor C. T. Ingold and the Clarendon Press for Figs. 10F and J; the *New Phytologist* for Fig. 3D; Dr J. Proskauer and the *Bryologist* for Fig. 3E; Dr S. Williams and the *Transactions* of the British Bryological Society for Fig. 3F.

Preface

The aim of this book is to fill a gap which exists between the full, straightforward treatment of the morphology of bryophytes and the research literature in all its detail and diversity of topics. My hope is that it will enable the university student to see morphological facts from a new angle and at the same time have his interest directed to other branches of bryophyte study.

The chapters in this book take the form of essays on various bryological topics, and, although no claim is made that the treatments given are in any instance exhaustive, a serious attempt has been made to introduce the student to a reasonably copious and representative literature. In the morphological chapters with which the book begins a comparative approach has been adopted, in order that old facts may be seen from a new angle; in order too that the habit of making comparisons may grow in the student of this subject.

It is true that each of the later chapters can provide only a sketchy outline of a big subject. Nevertheless, by dealing with some of these subjects at all one may be able to help the enquirer who is apt to find so little about most of them in the standard texts. I refer to bryophyte ecology, anatomy and physiology; also cytogenetics, geographical distribution and the meagre fossil record of these plants.

To select suitable subjects for the limited number of line drawings that can be included has not been easy. I would have liked more, but perhaps these few may serve to clarify the text in places. I am indebted to those authors and publishing houses that have kindly allowed copies of certain drawings to be made.

It is a great pleasure to record my gratitude to my friend Mr

P. J. Wanstall, who has most kindly read the entire text and suggested a number of improvements. I would also thank Professor H. Munro Fox, F.R.S., at whose invitation the book was undertaken, for his helpful criticism in the early stages and keen interest throughout. Finally, I am grateful to Professor T. M. Harris, F.R.S., for his unfailing interest and help on a number of occasions.

E.V.W.

May 1963

1

Introduction and classification

THE structure and life of bryophytes are usually approached by means of the detailed presentation of selected examples from the two groups, mosses and liverworts. In general textbooks of botany a single example from each has often been thought sufficient; in fuller treatments of cryptogams some details of classification are given and more examples taken. An orderly picture of the whole can be built up in this way, but another, quite different, approach is possible and that is the one adopted in this book. Here we are concerned in the different chapters with a review of different aspects of bryophyte study, which on the whole lend themselves to separate treatments, although some overlap is inevitable.

A certain amount of previous experience of the group is assumed. It is the aim of the chapters that follow to enable the student who has already begun a study of these plants to reach out further in many directions, to see something of the scope of the principal branches of bryology and to be led to the more important literature. In the course of the discussions reference will be made to diverse examples. Occasionally the germ of a new idea may come to the surface or a possible future line of investigation suggest itself. We shall start with structure considered mainly in relation to evolutionary problems, and proceed to other topics—vegetative propagation, sex organs, morphogenesis, anatomy and physiology, ecology, bryogeography and some others in later chapters. Some of these are big topics and space will permit only a limited treatment of them; but enough may be set down to indicate something of the breadth of the field which in each instance awaits the attention of the enquiring student.

First of all we may define the limits of the group Bryophyta.

It is widely known that bryophytes include the mosses (Musci) and the liverworts (Hepaticae). Many people think of the plant body of a moss as equipped with stem and leaves, whilst that of a liverwort they visualize as thalloid—a flattened, freely branched structure of variable size and shape. It is sometimes forgotten that the leafy liverworts far exceed the thalloid in number of species. Also, the word 'moss' is applied to much that has no connection with bryophytes. Thus reindeer moss is a lichen, club-mosses are pteridophytes (related to ferns and horsetails) and Spanish moss is a highly modified seed plant of the family Bromeliaceae.

The bryophytes are a well-defined and circumscribed group of plants. No recognizable link connects them on the one hand with algae, on the other with pteridophytes. Their evolution remains to a great extent a matter of speculation, and the interrelationships between the different living groups are by no means clearly understood. This arises partly from the fact that some groups, such as the so-called 'leafy liverworts' (Jungermanniales) and the 'true mosses' (Bryidae), are represented by an immense range of forms which are on the whole remarkably uniform, whilst others stand apart, a mere handful of forms or perhaps a few hundred species, in comparative isolation. The genus *Sphagnum* is such an example; *Anthoceros* and its immediate allies furnish another.

Examples from the Bryophyta take their place in elementary books on botany mainly because they illustrate a pattern of life cycle which is peculiarly their own. True, it finds a parallel in certain algae in which there is an alternation between two structurally similar generations; but the bryophyte life-cycle remains unique in that it displays two alternating generations, roughly equivalent in importance if not in size, both highly characteristic in their morphology, yet totally unlike one another. This life-cycle is far removed from the dominance of the haploid generation found in most green algae; it is almost as far removed from the overwhelming dominance of the sporophyte generation that occurs throughout the Pteridophytes. A study of *Pellia* reveals gametophyte dominance, for the green thallus is perennial, independent and freely branching, whilst the sporophyte is of strictly limited growth and duration, and in a fairly complete sense parasitic. *Buxbaumia*, a genus of partly saprophytic mosses, however, conveys quite another impression, with its sporophyte inordinately large beside the insignificant gametophyte (Fig. 12A). So there is some latitude in this matter of the emphasis that rests on each of the two generations; but the salient facts learnt regarding the life-cycles of the liverwort *Pellia* and the moss *Funaria* are not only very similar but also hold good throughout the bryophytes, with only rather unimportant variations.

We may now outline those features of the bryophyte life-cycle which are true of the group as a whole. A haploid spore germinates to produce a stage, commonly filamentous but sometimes ovoid, spherical or plate-like, which precedes the formation of the leafy shoots or gametophores. The latter are typically green, live for anything from a few months to several years, and bear the sex organs, antheridia and archegonia. In every instance, a motile male gamete from an antheridium having fertilized the egg, or oosphere, which lies at the base of the flask-shaped archegonium, a zygote is formed and the sporophyte generation supervenes. In all but the simplest cases this diploid phase early develops polarity and differentiates into a basal foot, a stalk-like seta and a distal spore-producing organ, the capsule. When the sporogenous tissue (archesporium) has completed the necessary number of cell divisions leading to the formation of spore mother cells the latter undergo each a meiotic, or reduction division, and tetrads of spores are formed which normally separate before discharge. Dehiscence and spore dispersal frequently entail the formation and functioning of structures, such as the elaters of liverworts and the peristome of mosses, which belong peculiarly to the Bryophyta. It may be noted, moreover, that both archegonium and antheridium are seen in a more complete and elaborate form here than in any other group of plants.

The structure of each generation and the mode of fertilization have imposed certain restrictions on the size of bryophytes. The largest normal erect-growing leafy stems are probably those of the larger species of the Australasian genus *Dawsonia* (40–70 cm); but Martin records[150] a remarkable example (seen by him in New Zealand) of a stem of *Polytrichum commune* attaining a length of six feet (150 cm) under water. Again, great length is attained by the underwater shoots of an aquatic moss such as *Fontinalis anti-pyretica* and by the pendent masses of many tropical epiphytes; but bryophytes as a whole are small and many are indeed microscopic. Few mosses have leaves exceeding 10 mm in length, whilst those of leafy liverworts are much smaller. The capsules of mosses are rarely above 6 mm long; those of liverworts are usually quite minute. Yet, small though they are, bryophytes can be important ecologically. Only seldom, as in some kinds of bog, arctic tundra and tropical mossy forest, do they compose the main element in the vegetation, but their value as indicator species is coming increasingly to be recognized.

Following his grounding in *Pellia* and *Funaria*, the student usually proceeds to a study of further examples, with the emphasis mainly on comparative morphology. Prepared slides have often been the basis of such a study, for it is only in the permanent preparation, made from material that has been embedded and microtomed, that many of the relevant details may be seen. Such studies are, of course, invaluable as a training in interpretative morphology. It is, however, essential that they be supplemented by a generous allowance of time devoted to the examination and dissection of freshly gathered plants. Thereby, the student can begin to see how the microscopic features are related to the life of the organism, and by working with a flora he can gradually acquire a knowledge of bryophyte taxonomy.

If a student is to attain proficiency in this study, he must be prepared to spend time in the field, and even more in the close microscopic study of the plants that he finds. In my view he will do well to move away at an early stage from too implicit a reliance on keys, and try to gain some real insight into the facts and ideas behind the scheme of classification. Then he will fairly soon be able to refer a proportion of the plants found directly to their genus, or to one of a small group of genera. In my experience every competent systematist —in whatever group of organisms—possesses this faculty for seeing the range of form exhibited by his group as a whole, and it is useless to suppose that one can proceed very far without it. The prerequisites are a keen eye for form and plenty of application. A real sense of power results when one becomes aware, for the first time, of having some real command of a group, such as mosses or liverworts, or for that matter the flowering plants or the birds of Britain. Perhaps there are two criteria by which we can judge that this time has come; first, when one can recognize at sight the bulk of what one finds; and secondly, when one can walk anywhere in the land with the knowledge that nothing—or almost nothing—that one finds will be wholly unfamiliar.

Two useful aids for the student of bryophytes are the herbarium and the collection of species alive in cultivation. The former is indispensable for serious taxonomic study, and most keen students will wish to build up their own reference collection. A range of species in cultivation, in unglazed pans in the cool greenhouse, is also an asset, especially where one may wish to see changes that take place in a particular plant throughout the year. Thallose liverworts are the easiest and most satisfactory bryophytes to grow by this method, whilst many mosses seem to suffer because one cannot replicate the conditions that they found in nature. Useful instructions are given by Richards[195] and those bryologists who have the facilities should experiment for themselves. By such methods one can add greatly to one's knowledge of the species studied; especially as regards their range of structural variation and their growth rate.

Equipped with some all-round knowledge, one can go on to specialize, on a chosen group or species, as an ecologist or in some other direction. The morphologist will be encouraged by Fulford's remark[71] that of all the known genera of the great order Jungermanniales (leafy liverworts) only some 5% had been fully investigated morphologically. The ecologist will find that comprehensive autecological studies have covered a far smaller proportion of the known species. The taxonomic specialist will find genus after genus of bryophytes awaiting a critical revision—even on a regionally limited basis. Finally, of course, there are those who turn to bryophytes only for some special advantage that they may offer for a physiological or genetical experiment.

Mosses and liverworts have long challenged taxonomists to devise a classification which will be at once reasonably natural and clearly workable. This challenge has not been easy to meet. It will be convenient to begin by considering the liverworts. As long ago as 1911 Cavers put forward a classification, the broad outlines of which are still followed today, although in no modern arrangement are they precisely the same as in Cavers' system.

There is, however, some agreement on the existence of six main types of liverwort construction:

1. *Anthoceros* and its allies.
2. *Sphaerocarpos* and its allies.
3. The elaborate thalloid structure seen at its highest development in *Marchantia*, *Preissia* and close allies.
4. The simple thalloid structure exemplified by *Pellia* but leading on to something like true 'leafiness' in some genera.
5. *Calobryum* and *Haplomitrium*, with their radially organized leafy shoots.
6. The 'leafy liverwort' series, with its strong tendency towards dorsiventrality of the leafy shoot.

No author has recognized these six groups more clearly than Jones, who has accepted them as the basis for six orders of liverworts*. His system, put forward in 'An annotated list of British hepatics'[119], will be adopted (in so far as the adoption of a system is necessary) in this book. He arranges liverworts as follows:

Class Hepaticae:
    Order 1   Anthocerotales
         2   Sphaerocarpales
         3   Marchantiales
         4   Metzgeriales
         5   Calobryales
         6   Jungermanniales
    Sub-order (a)   Ptilidiineae
               (b)   Jungermanniineae
               (c)   Porellineae

Quite indistinct (and sometimes debatable) lines of demarcation

*See end of Chapter 3 for mention of additional non-British order.

separate most of the liverwort orders one from another, but the Anthocerotales stand apart. This fact can be recognized without necessarily elevating the group to the rank of a class and thus equating it (Anthocerotae) with the classes Musci and Hepaticae. As Cavers[43] pointed out, Leitgeb in his early, monumental work on the hepatics[132-4] recognized the anomalous position of the Anthocerotales, although it was Howe[108], in 1899, who raised the group to class status, defining it and naming it Anthocerotes. Many hepaticologists have followed him in this.

It will be convenient now to turn to the question of the arrangement of the principal groups of mosses. Nobody has ever found a plant that is manifestly intermediate between liverworts and mosses, so that the two classes stand, without question, as separate major entities within the division Bryophyta. They differ in rhizoid structure, in manner of development of sex organs, in the prevailing mode of growth and cell structure of their leaves; in liverworts the seta develops rapidly at a late stage, and the capsule typically contains elaters in addition to the spores; whilst in mosses the seta develops slowly over a long period, and the capsule contains no elaters but normally has a characteristic ring of peristome teeth; and the moss sporophyte has a green phase not paralleled in liverworts outside the Anthocerotales. These and other features amply separate the two great groups.

Some 14,000 species of moss are known and the great majority are sufficiently alike in structure to create a real difficulty for the taxonomist, especially in the matter of fixing the limits of families and genera. A few groups of mosses, however, stand apart in isolation. This fact is reflected in all classifications of mosses that have been proposed. The groups in question are (1) the bog-mosses referable to the genus *Sphagnum* and (2) a group comprising the small, dark-coloured and mainly rock-dwelling mosses of the genus *Andreaea*, together with one other genus, *Neuroloma*. Whether the genus *Sphagnum*, with its many species distributed throughout the world, is quite so isolated as most bryologists have believed it to be has been questioned[77]; but it certainly appears so in its biology, its peculiar gross morphology and fine leaf anatomy, and in other gametophyte characters, besides important features of the sporophyte. *Andreaea*, represented in Britain by several species, and widely distributed in suitable parts of every continent, has nothing very remarkable about its leafy shoots, but shows distinctive features in protonema and sex organs. Like *Sphagnum*, it has the capsule raised on a gametophyte stalk (pseudopodium); and it displays an almost unique mode of dehiscence, the capsule splitting along four lines and releasing the spores through the gaping slits so formed.

To a lesser extent, two other groups of mosses stand apart. These are (1) the curious group represented in Britain by *Bux-baumia* and *Diphyscium*, and (2) the group typified in its highest development (in the northern hemisphere) by *Polytrichum*, but with an interesting southern hemisphere counterpart in *Dawsonia*, which is probably less closely related than it at first appears.

The classification given by Reimers[191] in Engler's Syllabus takes account of these facts and admits five sub-classes of mosses. The system is shown here in outline:

Class: Musci
  Sub-class: Sphagnidae
    Order: Sphagnales   1 Family
  Sub-class: Andreaeidae
    Order: Andreaeales   1 Family
  Sub-class: Bryidae
    12 Orders, as follows:

Archidiales	1 Family
Dicranales	7 Families
Fissidentales	1 Family
Pottiales	3 Families
Grimmiales	1 Family
Funariales	6 Families
Schistostegales	1 Family
Tetraphidales	1 Family
Eubryales	16 Families
Isobryales	23 Families
Hookeriales	6 Families
Hypnobryales	12 Families

Sub-class:	Buxbaumiidae	
Order:	Buxbaumiales	2 Families
Sub-class:	Polytrichidae	
Order:	Polytrichales	1 Family
	Dawsoniales	1 Family

The differences are indeed slight between most modern systems of classification and they are concerned mainly with rank and terminology, only rarely with the position, or even the existence of a given order, of mosses. This does not mean that there is unanimity on the question of the probable course of evolution in the Musci, but rather that most contemporary bryologists are agreed to follow in the main the system of arrangement which came into being shortly after the turn of the century and owed its foundation to men such as Fleischer[67] and Brotherus[25], who were acquainted with mosses on a world scale. If one compares this arrangement with those set forth in Dixon's *Student's handbook of British mosses* or in Grout's *Moss flora of North America*[90], the most substantial difference seems to lie in the fact that earlier authors took no account of the ordinal rank; thus in many instances the content of a particular family in the hands of such an author will be identical with the content of a corresponding order today.

A dilemma which has always bothered the bryologist concerned with moss classification is that of the rival claims of gametophyte and sporophyte to provide evidence on which he may base his conclusions. Dixon himself, at a later date[59], expressed this clearly when he presented a more modern scheme of classification as his contribution to Verdoorn's *Manual of bryology*. It is safe to say that this dilemma has never been completely overcome but at an earlier date the emphasis tended to be placed very heavily on the sporophyte and especially on the peristome. More recently gametophyte characters have been given more weight. The distinction was made early between the prevailingly erect or ascending 'acrocarps', with their terminal archegonia and sporophytes, and the commonly prostrate, freely branched 'pleurocarps' with archegonia and sporophytes borne laterally. It is still useful on occasion, although its validity was seriously questioned fifty years ago[43].

In the system which we are adopting almost all the 'pleurocarps' are found in three orders: Isobryales, Hookeriales and Hypnobryales. It is perhaps remarkable that a reasonable degree of uniformity exists in the various proposed classifications of both mosses and hepatics. There is little doubt that the two considerations which militate most strongly against any real certainty of conclusions are (1) the comparative scarcity of fossil bryophytes and (2) the difficulty of according due weight to the often conflicting evidence afforded by the two generations—gametophyte and sporophyte.

Note on classification systems. Space prevents our dealing with all the varied systems in use today. Thus, for liverworts, Arnell[7] and Müller[159] differ in various respects from Jones; whilst for mosses, Richards and Wallace[197] and Nyholm[166] will each show minor differences from Reimers. Many writers, including Smith[218] and Parihar[173], accord class status to the group that contains *Anthoceros* and its allies, and I am aware that a weakness of Jones's system lies in the fact that Metzgeriales are separated from Jungermanniales by just as wide a gap as that separating either of them from Anthocerotales; this at least is implied by giving each an ordinal rank. The strength of the system lies in its simplicity. Furthermore, it will be observed that by simultaneously following Jones for liverworts and Reimers for mosses, we are implying that greater differences separate *Polytrichum* and its allies (Polytrichidae) from ordinary mosses (Bryidae) than those which separate, for example, *Anthoceros* from *Calobryum* among hepatics. For these liverworts are merely placed in different orders —the mosses are in separate sub-classes. The explanation of this kind of anomaly lies, I believe, in the fact that hepaticologists have not as a whole begun to use the ordinal rank in the modern way in which moss systematists have used it; and indeed as it is used by taxonomists working with most other groups of organisms.

2

Gametophyte structure of
thalloid liverworts

IN THIS chapter we consider thalloid structure among the gametophytes of liverworts from a comparative point of view. Accounts of
the thallus of *Pellia* appear in all elementary textbooks of botany and
these are supplemented in bryophyte textbooks[173],[218] by those of
further selected types. Usually included are *Riccia*, *Marchantia* or a
close ally such as *Preissia*, and *Anthoceros*. Sometimes *Riccardia*
finds a place. In few cases, other than the masterly morphological
treatment of Cavers[43], and the more functional or 'biological'
account of Goebel[85], has the comparative approach been adopted.

Four important patterns of thalloid gametophyte structure are
due for consideration and these are exemplified respectively by the
four orders Anthocerotales, Sphaerocarpales, Marchantiales and
Metzgeriales. It is possible to regard thalloid structure as nearer
to some hypothetical algal ancestry than is the differentiation into
stem and leaves which has come to prevail in the overwhelming
majority of living hepatics. One may also wish to place these various
thalloid forms in some sequence of ascending complexity, perhaps
invoking an evolutionary process; but this is beset with difficulties.

Sphaerocarpos is taken first because of its extreme simplicity.
Always small, and in the male plants sometimes as little as 1 mm
in diameter, the delicate green thallus* found here comes as near as
any to an undifferentiated expanse of green cells that might have
characterized a hypothetical algal ancestor. This thought so attracted
the early evolutionary botanist Lotsy[139] that he wrote of an imaginary

* Often appearing so, but for view of *Sphaerocarpos* as fundamentally
leafy, see Proskauer, J., J. Linn. Soc. Bot., 1954.

Sphaero-Riccia which would serve as an ancestral bryophyte (if it could be found), combining the simple gametophyte of *Sphaero-carpos* with the remarkably undifferentiated sporophyte of *Riccia*. The thallus of *Sphaerocarpos* however is not quite so simple, nor so lacking in specialized features, as might at first glance appear. New cells come from groups of apical initials, much as they do in *Marchantia*. Simple rhizoids emerge from the central 'cushion' of thallus, which is several cells thick in contrast with the delicate wings that are but one cell in thickness. The sex organs (well figured in longitudinal section by Smith) arise in sequence from the apex partially protected by mucilage hairs. Associated with each arche-gonium, and with each antheridium, is the enveloping protective case, or involucre, which is so characteristic a feature of *Sphaero-carpos* and is unique to the Sphaerocarpales. *Sphaerocarpos michelii* appears occasionally in some quantity on the soil of fallow fields in Britain in the form of small, pale green, nearly circular patches. Little of the thallus itself can be seen, for it is almost completely covered by these close-packed, conical or pear-shaped involucres.

One might say that the thallus of *Pellia* was little more than an enlargement of the simple thallus of *Sphaerocarpos*. There is the same comparative lack of differentiation between different cells or tissues (Fig. 2A), although it is true that in *Pellia* chlorophyll abounds only in the superficial layers of the dorsal and ventral surfaces. Since the tissues are without air spaces, the thallus appears deep green and translucent, not light green and opaque as do those of typical members of the Marchantiales. The rhizoids are simple and uniform, as in *Sphaerocarpos*; and antheridia, followed by groups of archegonia, are elaborated from cells cut off in sequence from the large, four-sided apical cell. They mature along the upper surface of the thallus midrib, the antheridial chambers further from, the archegonial 'receptacles' nearer to, the apex. There are, however, no special involucres of the kind seen in *Sphaerocarpos*; growth is much more extensive and mature plants many times larger than the minute, filmy-thin thalli of *Sphaerocarpos*. Were thallus structure alone available the two plants would undoubtedly be placed to-gether, and in an early arrangement Schiffner[205] did indeed place the 'Sphaerocarpoid' liverworts at the beginning of the order

Jungermanniales; but resemblances to the Marchantiales in the development of the sex organs, and in two sporophyte characters— their embryology and single-layered capsule wall—have since sufficed to erect the separate order Sphaerocarpales.

No such similarity to any other known group is shown by the thallus of *Preissia quadrata*, which typifies the 'higher' Marchantiales. It is far more complex than either of the two thalli considered so far and quite different biologically. For here the thallus is not merely many cells thick (approximately thirty cells in the midrib, ten cells in the wings), but it is sharply differentiated into a narrow, chlorophyll-rich upper (dorsal) region and a colourless, lower (ventral) region (Fig. 2B). The ventral surface of the thallus bears two kinds of rhizoids and rows of ventral scales. The upper surface is divided into 'areolae', each of which marks the limits of an underlying air chamber, the entry to which is by way of a centrally placed, barrel-shaped air pore. The walls of each chamber are colourless cells, and from the floor arise short chains of ovoid or subspherical cells extremely rich in chloroplasts. Beneath this well aerated and highly developed photosynthetic system the layers of colourless cells extending to the ventral surface are themselves differentiated (in the midrib) to include storage cells of several kinds, whilst here and there a thick-walled fibre may be seen. Often, on either side of the middle line there will be extensive patches of cells with purple walls, many of them containing the hyphae of a mycorrhizal fungus.

In short, here is a thallus far more complex in structure than anything found elsewhere among liverworts, and similar only to that of its own immediate allies such as *Marchantia* and *Conocephalum*. It would seem, moreover, to be fitted biologically to carry on efficient absorption from the substratum by means of abundant rhizoids and, at the same time, preserve the dorsal layers of the thallus for a functional life akin to that of the green leaf among vascular plants. Finally, the ventral scales provide some protection for the delicate apical tissues. The sex organs, borne up on stalked receptacles (the male smaller and more shortly stalked), serve only to enhance the impression that here is the climax of thalloid evolution among liverworts.

The well-known thallus of *Anthoceros* is superficially more like the first two described but has many fundamental points of difference from either of them. Thus, the rosettes or irregularly shaped thalli are typically dark green and without obvious gloss. In some species (but not in *A. laevis*) there are extensive cavities internally, but these are filled with mucilage, not air. Some are occupied by the blue-green alga *Nostoc* and this may benefit the liverwort, although Peirce[179] claimed to have raised healthy plants in its absence. The outline of the thallus is wavy, the surface sometimes crimped in a characteristic way. Each thallus lobe has an apical cell whose derivatives provide the new growth. Only rhizoids with smooth walls are found.

A most important feature of *Anthoceros* is the single large chloroplast which ordinarily occurs in each green cell of the gametophyte. Some have seen in this a resemblance to the chromatophores of certain green algae, but there are difficulties about making too close a comparison (cf. Smith)[218]. It is certainly very different from the small discoid chloroplasts that occur in large numbers in the green cells of other bryophytes. A second remarkable feature is that both kinds of sex organ develop within, rather than above, the surface tissues. This makes the mature archegonia appear fully immersed, their venters and necks confluent with surrounding vegetative cells; whilst the antheridia are found, several together, on the floor of cavities that are roofed over at first but are ultimately broken through to form conspicuous antheridial 'craters' whose orange contents are at times very obvious indeed.

Cavers minimized the importance of both these peculiarities, pointing out that sometimes in *Anthoceros* several chloroplasts occupy a cell, and that some other liverworts, for example species of *Riccardia* (allied to *Pellia*), have a partially immersed archegonium. The full justification for the separation of the Anthocerotales from all other groups of liverworts can be appreciated only after taking into account the unique features of the sporophyte; but the gametophyte is surely remarkable enough to suggest that *Anthoceros* is not very closely connected with the other three forms that we have examined.

We may now enquire how far these four examples represent

the range of thalloid gametophyte structure among liverworts and what light is thrown upon them by a survey of the immediate allies of each. This will be instructive, both from the biological and the evolutionary standpoints; but it must be emphasized that evolutionary conclusions must rest also on facts drawn from the sporophytes.

In every order except the Marchantiales we see a close relationship between acknowledged thalloid and closely allied leafy, or quasi-leafy, forms. Thus, associated with *Sphaerocarpos* is *Riella*, with its unique spiral or wavy wing of tissue extending out from the axis, and its minute but evident foliar appendages. *Pellia* is not far removed from forms which were interpreted by the earlier morphologists as an ascending series, leading up through the almost leafy *Blasia*, by way of *Petalophyllum*, to the undoubted leafy axis of *Fossombronia* (Fig. 1). Nowadays there is considerable doubt as to whether the series should be read in this direction. Finally, in *Dendroceros*, a genus of epiphytes allied to *Anthoceros*, one finds a stout axis and lobed wings of tissue one cell thick; surely a striking parallel to the condition in *Fossombronia*. In all three instances a tendency towards leafiness would seem to be inherent in the thallus, and never far away from finding expression. Whether leafiness should be regarded as derived, or the primitive state, is hard to say. The natural tendency is to take the former view, but a weighty section of modern opinion inclines to the reverse. We shall return to this topic at a later point; but having established a link between thalloid and leafy conditions we must now explore the diversity of form in these different groups. Only two, the Metzgeriales (with *Pellia* as example) and the Marchantiales (with *Preissia* as example), call for extended comment.

The genera related to *Pellia* reveal an interesting range of forms in the British flora alone, but examined on a world scale the diversity is seen to be much greater still. Within the limits of what was known at the time, this range of forms was well displayed by both Goebel and Cavers. It was natural to read these as an ascending evolutionary series and Cavers lost no opportunity to do so. On any view they afford a striking series. There are forms which consist of a simple undifferentiated thallus, as do all the simpler species of *Riccardia*. There are species, like *R. multifida* in Britain, where the thallus is remarkable for its pinnate branching. *Metzgeria* (of which *M. furcata* is a common bark-dwelling hepatic in Britain) has a thallus with well-defined midrib and wings (Fig. 1F). *Pallavicinia* is notable for the conducting tissue in its central strand. Although without specialized thickenings, these cells are like tracheids in shape. But like *Pellia*, all are thalloid liverworts in which the thallus itself shows no particular differentiation beyond a midrib and, of course, a crop of rhizoids on its ventral surface.

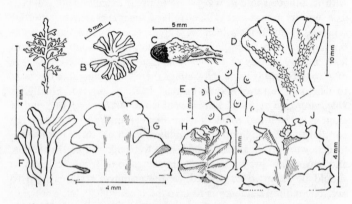

Fig. 1 Form of gametophyte in some Marchantiales and Metzgeriales. A. *Riccardia multifida*. B. *Riccia sorocarpa*. C. *Targionia hypophylla*, with perianth. D. *Conocephalum conicum*. E. Part of same, enlarged to show areolae and pores. F. *Metzgeria furcata*. G. *Blasia pusilla*. H. *Petalophyllum ralfsii*. J. *Fossombronia angulosa*.

Three different directions of further development may be noted briefly. First, there are at least two parallel series of exotic liverworts, the one apparently springing from *Riccardia*, the other from *Pallavicinia* and its allies, in which the plant body is much more differentiated, having a creeping portion clothed in rhizoids, a nearly cylindrical stem-like portion and an expanded, dichotomously branched frond. Representative genera are *Umbraculum* and *Symphyogyna* respectively, and both were well illustrated by Cavers. They seem to represent culminating points of gametophyte differentiation in the Metzgeriales.

A second development is the advent of leafiness. It is vaguely foreshadowed in *Moerckia*, with its wavy thallus margins; or again in *Blasia*, where thallus wings are deeply and regularly lobed but true leaves are lacking. In *Petalophyllum* the leaf-like appendages are two rows of nearly erect lamellae on the upper surface of the thallus. *Petalophyllum ralfsii* (Fig. 1H) is an uncommon plant of wet hollows in sand-dunes. It is also minute, but is worth searching for in order that its unique structure may be seen. Finally, true leaves, borne in two ranks on a nearly cylindrical axis, are seen in *Fossombronia*. This genus is well represented in Britain, although several species are much alike in their gametophytes and can be satisfactorily separated only by their spores.

The third direction of specialization consists of the total loss of chlorophyll. This condition is found in *Cryptothallus mirabilis* which is thus a plant of unique interest, although in other gameto-phyte characters it is close to *Riccardia*. Williams[261] gave an ex-cellent account of this plant when it was first found in Britain. He pointed out that the thallus was more succulent than that of *Ric-cardia*, a fact no doubt correlated with its mycorrhizal habit. Nearly two-thirds of the transverse section of the thallus consists of cells occupied by the mycorrhizal fungus. Between the sporophytes of the two genera there are several differences, most notably the fact that the capsule in *Cryptothallus* sheds its spores through four slits, rather after the manner of the moss *Andreaea*. The first British record of this saprophytic liverwort was from a locality near Helens-burgh, Dumbartonshire, in December, 1948, but it has since been recorded in other parts of the country. *Cryptothallus* first came to the attention of bryologists some thirty years earlier, after Zederbauer had found it in a wood near Vienna, mistaking it for prothalli of a species of *Lycopodium*.

Müller[159] recognizes six families of Metzgeriales in Europe and all have at least one representative in Britain. The presence or absence of a midrib and of leaf-like appendages furnish two important characters on which family distinctions are based. Another is provided by the diverse position of the sex organs. For although these are on the upper surface of the thallus in *Pellia* and some other genera, they occur on specialized short branches in *Metzgeria* and

Riccardia. In the former these branches arise ventrally; in the latter they are typically side branches. When one takes into account a number of other characters, including several of importance derived from the sporophyte generation, it is clear that the Metzgeriales comprise a number of small groups, each somewhat isolated from the others. The simpler species of *Riccardia* (such as *R. pinguis* and *R. sinuata* in Britain) seem to form the logical starting point of the series. Only the palaeobotanist (cf. Chapter 11) can tell us the age of their simple thalloid form.

As we have seen, *Preissia quadrata*, typifying the higher Marchantiales, presents the most elaborate thalloid gametophyte to be found among liverworts. Thus it possesses: (1) photosynthetic air chambers; (2) each chamber opening by a barrel-shaped pore with an adjustable aperture (Walker and Pennington[236]); (3) two kinds of rhizoids, smooth and tuberculate, and ventral scales with appendages; (4) antheridia borne within a stalked recceptale; (5) archegonia (and hence sporogonia) borne on a stalked receptacle— the whole mushroom-shaped structure being known when fruiting as the carpocephalum. Each of these five features will be examined in turn to see how it has become modified, or appears simplified, in related members of the Marchantiales.

Probably the large genus *Marchantia* alone, with its bigger (and well-known) male and female mushroom-shaped or umbrella-like receptacles, comes close to *Preissia* on all these five points. In the arrangement of Müller[159] only *Marchantia*, *Bucegia* and *Dumortiera* are placed with *Preissia* in the Marchantiaceae, as represented in Europe. The abundantly gemmiferous *Lunularia*, *Conocephalum*— remarkable for its robust, glossy dark green thallus—and the delicate non-British genus *Exormotheca* are made each the basis of a separate family. In some of these genera, and even more in the simpler Marchantiales such as *Targionia*, *Corsinia* and *Riccia* (again separate families), we can see one or more of the above five features modified or simplified.

(1) *Photosynthetic air chambers*. The classical illustration of reduction in these chambers is furnished by *Dumortiera*, in which the response to differing environmental conditions was investigated long ago by Coker[51]. Excessive moisture induces atrophy of the

chamber as such, the roof being lost entirely whilst only scattered short chains of green cells spring from where the floor has been. In well-watered *Dumortiera hirsuta* grown in shade I have found indeed that the chambers are habitually lacking, even in the youngest parts of the plant, an epidermal layer of photosynthetic cells covering the upper surface of the thallus. In *Preissia* the photosynthetic region occupies only about a quarter of the midrib thickness of the

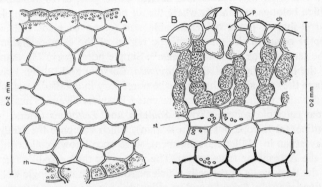

Fig. 2 Comparison between thalli of *Pellia* and *Preissia* in transverse section. A. *Pellia fabbroniana*, T.S. midrib region. rh. origin of rhizoid. B. *Preissia quadrata*, T.S. wing region, showing barrel-shaped pore (p.) air chamber (ch.) with columns of chlorophyllose cells. Below some cells store starch (st.). The walls of cells on ventral surface (shown dark) hold anthocyanin pigment (deep purple in life).

thallus; and one line of departure is found in those species where more than half the thickness is occupied by an irregular network of chlorophyllous tissue. This produces a complex chamber system in place of the single layer of chambers seen in *Preissia* and *Marchantia*, but the walls of the chambers themselves provide the green tissue and there are here no additional plates or filaments. This is seen in *Reboulia*, and here and there elsewhere. In the majority of species of *Riccia* the whole upper surface of the thallus consists of close-set columns of green cells. A pear-shaped colourless cell commonly terminates each column and the whole system is freely provided with fine air channels. There are no chambers and pores as such here. The thallus segments that compose the neat rosettes of *Riccia* species are narrow and often U-shaped or V-shaped in transverse section; thus the delicate columns of photosynthetic tissue can be given some protection in dry conditions by the infolding of the thallus margins.

(2) *Type of pore*. Only in *Preissia* has the barrel-shaped pore been shown to be adjustable in aperture size; but rather similar pores are found in *Marchantia* and several other genera. In *Reboulia*, which belongs to a family where the air pores are normally simple, barrel-shaped pores of remarkable size (seven to eight cells in depth) occur in the photosynthetic region of the carpocephalum. The same is true of *Conocephalum*[42]. Simple pores prevail in many of the lower Marchantiales—*Targionia*, *Corsinia* and others. Even where they are simple, however, the pores vary in detailed structure and hence in the appearance presented in surface view. Thus the three calcicole genera *Clevea*, *Sauteria* and *Peltolepis* (found in continental Europe but not in Britain), which compose the family Cleveaceae in Müller's arrangement, were once known collectively as the Astroporae (star-pored). The pores owe their star-like form to the thick walls of the cells which surround each as a single well-defined ring. In *Reboulia* and its allies each simple pore is bounded by several concentric rings of cells. The pore becomes a very unspecialized structure in *Corsinia* and in those species of *Riccia* (such as *R. crystallina* and *R. huebeneriana*) where it persists.

(3) *Ventral scales* are most prominent, and functionally most important, close behind the apex of a thallus segment. Cavers[42] figured prominent scales lying over and effectively protecting the apex in *Conocephalum*. They are seen even better in species of *Plagiochasma*, *Grimaldia* and *Targionia*, plants of dry habitats in which the scales together with the infolding thallus margins are clearly of protective value. Ventral scales are delicate plates of tissue only one cell thick. They are closely overlapping, and characteristically set in two rows. The scales are often deep purple. In most of the higher Marchantiales they are appendaged, although the appendage is sometimes hard to demonstrate. Appendages are also found in *Targionia*, but have been lost (or perhaps they never existed) in the lower Marchantiales such as *Corsinia* and *Riccia*.

Here too the scales themselves are either scattered or in a single irregular row. At times, especially in aquatics, they may be difficult to see at all. Two kinds of rhizoids are a distinguishing mark of the Marchantiales as a whole.

(4) *Antheridiophore*. In this feature a clear-cut series can be seen which may however be interpreted as running in either direction. *Preissia* and *Marchantia* have a stalked, green or purplish structure like a miniature mushroom. In *Conocephalum*, as in *Reboulia* (Fig. 16E) and most of its allies, the antheridia are grouped in sessile, cushion-like receptacles. In *Corsinia* they are irregularly grouped along a portion of the thallus midrib; whilst *Riccia* produces antheridia singly at various points on the surface of the thallus in or near the median line. Often the site of an embedded antheridium is marked by a projecting turret of surrounding thallus tissue.

(5) *Archegoniophore*. Stalked archegonial receptacles (and thence carpocephala, or fruiting heads) are much more widespread than the corresponding stalked antheridial structures. They are found throughout the Marchantiaceae and all closely related families; but the number of archegonial groups in the rayed head varies from eight in *Marchantia polymorpha*, through four in *Preissia* and *Lunularia*, to two in the diminutive *Exormotheca*. They are found also in *Reboulia* and its allies; again in *Clevea*, *Sauteria* and *Peltolepis*. These two groups run parallel in some respects; thus *Plagiochasma* (related to *Reboulia*) and *Clevea* are both unusual in that the archegoniophore does not remove the growing power of the apex and hence appears to spring from a point well back on the upper surface of the thallus. *Targionia* is unique in that the archegonia arise ventrally behind the thallus apex, and the sporophyte is enclosed by a pair of close-fitting dark purple structures like the valves of a mussel shell (Fig. 1c). In *Corsinia* the archegonia are borne on specialized parts of the upper surface of the thallus; associated with them is a flap of tissue which may be either an incipient or a vestigial archegoniophore. Finally, in *Riccia* the archegonia like the antheridia are scattered, solitary and embedded in the thallus.

From early times (Leitgeb)[134] much emphasis has been laid upon the detailed structure of the carpocephalum in the different genera of the higher Marchantiales in an attempt to arrive at a satisfactory classification of them. Thus, the stalk may have no furrow (as in *Clevea* and *Plagiochasma*), bear a single furrow with rhizoids as in *Reboulia*, *Conocephalum* and many others, or bear two such furrows, as it does in *Preissia*, *Marchantia* and a few other genera. Also, the archegonia may occur singly in each involucre as they do in all but the highest Marchantiales, or they may be clustered, as in a few specialized genera including *Marchantia* itself.

This then may conclude our survey of thallus structure and insertion of gametangia in the Marchantiales. This topic is one worth entering in some detail, for not only is the complex thallus of some members of this group without parallel elsewhere among bryophytes, but furthermore these liverworts are exceptionally easy to grow and, once a greenhouse collection has been started, they are freely available for study. Any evolutionary interpretation of the facts will be deferred until the sporophyte generation has been reviewed (cf. Chapter 4). Even if Cavers[43] was able to write that 'except in a very general way, the sporogonium affords very little guidance to the phylogeny of the Marchantiales', it does provide some of the basic evidence on which all schemes of classification of this group have rested.

This chapter may conclude with accounts of two remarkable and puzzling genera of thalloid liverworts—*Monoclea* and *Monocarpus**. It will be convenient to refer briefly to both gametophyte and sporophyte generations. *Monoclea forsteri* (Fig. 3D, E) was brought back from New Zealand by Forster on one of Captain Cook's voyages and erroneously named *Anthoceros univalvis*. W. J. Hooker in 1820 made it the type of a monotypic genus, *Monoclea*, naming it after its discoverer. In 1858 it was the subject of a detailed investigation by Gottsche and much later it received attention from the American morphologist, D. H. Campbell[34], who was the first to place it in the *Marchantiales*. Johnson[117] and Cavers[41] also studied and commented upon the genus, the former making use of material of a second species, *M. gottschei*, from Jamaica. On balance the relationship with Marchantiales was endorsed, only to be challenged

*Name changed by Proskauer (*Taxon*, 1961, **10**, 155) to *Carrpos*.

at a later date by Schiffner[206]. Evans, moreover, was inclined to the view that the genus was nearer to the Metzgeriales and some others have shared this view. Finally, in a recent study, Proskauer[187] has reviewed the position briefly, and whilst he rejects as inadmissible much of the evidence on which earlier conclusions in either direction were based, he believes that *Monoclea* belongs to the Marchantiales. He has had the advantage of examining fresh material of *M. forsteri* from New Zealand and from Chile, and of probable *M. gottschei* from the interior of Peru. It is obvious from the foregoing that *Monoclea* must present a very odd combination of characters.

Features of *Monoclea* which support a relationship with *Pellia* are: (1) absence of any trace of ventral scales; (2) no air-chamber system; (3) insertion of the archegonia on a sloping surface of thallus where they are protected by a collar-like involucre; and (4) the most striking character (and the only one which Proskauer admits to be of any weight), a seta several centimetres long. Then there are the following six characters which have been cited at various times in support of its relationship with the Marchantiales: (1) possession of both smooth and tuberculate rhizoids, which differ also in direction of growth; (2) presence of oil body cells and mycorrhizal cells within the massive thallus. These two characters alone are admitted by Proskauer. Four others, of more doubtful value, are: (3) male receptacle cushion-like, as in many genera of Marchantiales; (4) six rows of cells in the archegonial neck; (5) 'Marchantioid' embryology, with an octant stage represented; and (6) a single layer of cells in the capsule wall. The fifth point is to some extent discounted because many genera of Marchantiales do not themselves pass through an octant (ball of eight cells) stage in their embryology.

Summarizing, one may say that *Monoclea* combines a superficial appearance resembling *Pellia* with fundamental features that proclaim a relationship with Marchantiales. It is the peculiar interest of Proskauer's modern contribution to the discussion that he seizes upon the relevance to the present problem of Burgeff's massive researches on the mutation possibilities of *Marchantia*[32]. He writes: 'Prior to Burgeff it would have been too daring to suggest a relationship between *Dumortiera* and *Monoclea*.' This is the relationship he now suggests. Although *Dumorteria* has a perfectly normal carpocephalum, this structure bears sporophytes of unusual size for the group as a whole. The very long seta of *Monoclea* and its lack of any carpocephalum are on the whole out of harmony with the higher Marchantiales, and one may have to look, as earlier morphologists have done, more in the direction of

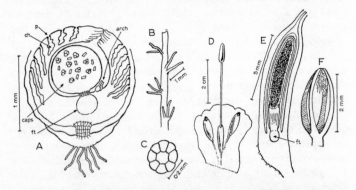

Fig. 3 Some remarkable liverwort genera. A. *Monocarpus*. L.S. fertile plant, somewhat diagrammatic (after Carr). B. *Takakia*, portion of axis with phyllids, and C. the same, T.S. phyllid (after Hattori and Mizutani). D. *Monoclea*, part of thallus, with sporophyte, showing long seta and capsule (after Cavers), and E. L.S. sporophyte, younger stage (after Proskauer). F. *Cryptothallus*, dehisced capsule (after Williams). arch. old, unfertilized archegonia; caps. capsule; ch. air chamber; p. air pore; ft. foot.

such a genus as *Targionia* for a closer resemblance to it within this order. The susceptibility of *Dumortiera* species to the loss of their air chamber systems in very moist environments, and the existence of another Marchantiaceous genus, *Monoselenium*, which lacks air chambers altogether[187] have been quoted in support of admitting *Monoclea* (with its chamberless thallus) to the Marchantiales. There, on balance, it is probably most satisfactorily placed. One conclusion at least seems inescapable; that the genus *Monoclea*, with its two species showing markedly disjunct distribution, and its odd combination of characters, must be a very ancient type of thalloid liverwort. As Parihar[173] reminds us, it is also exceedingly large, with a thallus attaining 20 cm long and 5 cm wide.

The recent discovery of the remarkable liverwort *Monocarpus sphaerocarpus* on the bare mud of a saltpan in north-west Victoria, Australia, throws a new light on the possible relationship between Sphaerocarpales and Marchantiales. An excellent account of this new genus has been given by Carr[38]*, and it is clear that the minute plant (Fig. 3A) combines the simple thallus and proportionately large involucre of *Sphaerocarpos* with the presence, within the involucre (but not the thallus), of a system of photosynthetic air chambers opening by pores akin to what is found in the higher Marchantiales. Müller[159] had already brought forward good evidence, from the structure of antheridia and spermatozoids among other things, to suggest that the connection of *Sphaerocarpos* with the Marchantiales was closer than some had supposed. Indeed, in his scheme of classification he made the Sphaerocarpineae a sub-order of Marchantiales. *Monocarpus* is like *Sphaerocarpos*, not only in the features mentioned above but also in many characters of the sporophyte, but, as Carr points out, its photosynthetic chambers and pores 'transgress the limits of the Sphaerocarpineae'. Its discovery is of the greatest interest and it is made the basis of a new family and a new sub-order, Monocarpineae, of the Marchantiales.

*See Proskauer (1961) *Phytomorphology*, **11**, 359, for fuller account and different conclusions.

B

3

Gametophyte of leafy liverworts

THE leafy liverworts (Jungermanniales of Jones, Jungermanniales Acrogynae of many earlier systems) are by far the richest in species of the orders of liverworts. Müller has estimated that 84% of all liverworts are leafy forms, and nearly all are members of this order. A fundamental feature of the gametophyte here is its growth from an apical cell which takes the form of an inverted pyramid consisting of a base and three sides from which derivatives are cut off. With the exception of a few genera (e.g. *Pleurozia*) this so-called three-sided apical cell occurs universally in the group, and since the derivatives from each cutting face contribute to both stem and leaves, the fundamental leaf arrangement is three-ranked. Contemporary morphologists regard a radially symmetrical leafy shoot, formed in this way, as primitive in the order and see all dorsi-ventral shoot systems as derived from it. Thus, we find in the check-list of Jones[119] and in the full treatments of Arnell[7] (for Scandinavia) and Müller[159] (for Europe) that those families and genera with a nearly perfect radial symmetry of the leafy shoot are placed at the beginning, and they are followed by others which are considered to have been modified to varying extents.

Nearly perfect radial symmetry of the leafy shoot is quite rare in the Jungermanniales and only a few British genera show this feature. Among them, two good examples are *Herberta* and *Anthelia*. *Herberta hutchinsiae* (Fig. 4A) is a prominent hepatic on mountain ledges in some parts of western Britain, conspicuous on account of its orange-brown colour and robust, erect habit. It may easily be mistaken for a moss at first glance, but closer inspection reveals the three ranks of leaves, all much alike in size and each cleft to the base into two long tapering lobes. *Anthelia julacea*, a plant of mountain springs and stream beds, and *A. juratzkana*, a rather rare species in Britain, characteristic of late snow areas on high mountains, are much smaller plants, but the minute leaves show the same nearly symmetrically three-ranked arrangement and each is again deeply cleft into two acute lobes. This type of leaf lobing finds its explanation in another characteristic attribute of the Jungermanniales, that each leaf, from a very early stage, grows by means of two distinct apical growing points. This readily leads to a bi-lobed or cleft leaf

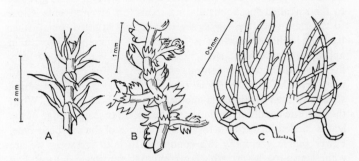

Fig. 4 Gametophytes of Jungermanniales. A. Part of shoot of *Herberta hutchinsiae*. B. Part of shoot of *Lepidozia reptans*. C. Leaf of *Trichocolea tomentella*.

at maturity; by contrast a simple, entire leaf of rounded form is relatively uncommon in the group as a whole.

The row of leaves lying in the mid-ventral line is given a special term—amphigastria or 'underleaves', and even in *Anthelia* these leaves are slightly smaller than their lateral counterparts. In such genera as *Trichocolea* and *Lepidozia* there is a greater difference between the sizes of amphigastria and lateral leaves, and in these genera the habit is prostrate or ascending rather than erect. These liverworts, and their immediate allies, illustrate another development, namely the tendency for the leaf to be divided into three or four lobes. The three or four finger-like lobes can be seen well, under a lens, in the minute leaves of the richly branched cushions of *Lepidozia reptans* (Fig. 4B), a common plant of acid woodland banks. In *Ptilidium* each leaf lobe bears numerous filamentous lateral appendages, and this tendency reaches its ultimate expression in such a plant as *Trichocolea tomentella*. Here the finer ramifications of the leaf lobes (Fig. 4c) remind one of a richly branched fila- mentous alga. This distinctive, pale green leafy liverwort is found in fen carr and certain other habitats where a permanently high relative humidity can be relied upon.

The adoption of a horizontal or plagiotropous shoot system is very widespread among the Jungermanniales, but it is interesting that this appears to have been achieved in two ways. These give rise to the so-called succubous and incubous leaf arrangements. Close to the stem apex the leaves are transversely inserted, but further back an oblique insertion is achieved by differential growth in appropriate sectors of stem tissue. In the larger group of leafy liverworts the lower, or ventral, edge of the leaf is carried forward relative to the upper or dorsal edge and the leaves on the resulting shoot will then overlap one another in a succubous manner. When the opposite condition prevails and the upper, or dorsal, edge of the leaf is carried forward the resulting overlap is of the incubous type. Fewer genera exemplify this condition. In both instances we are witnessing a precise growth adaptation to the prostrate or ascending habit, and one which results in the leaf surfaces being brought into a good position to receive the incident light. It must not be forgotten that there will have to be a compensatory growth at some stage in an opposing sector of stem tissue; otherwise the stem itself would become sharply curved, which in fact is not ordinarily so. As an example of the succubous condition one may take *Lopho- colea* (Fig. 5B); of the incubous condition, *Bazzania* (Fig. 5A). Both genera possess amphigastria only a small fraction of the size of the lateral leaves.

Lophocolea comprises over 150 species, *Bazzania* over 300, and both are distributed throughout the world. *Lophocolea heterophylla*, with decaying logs as its principal habitat, is easily obtained and will serve to illustrate many features that are typical of the order as a whole. The delicate, little-differentiated stem, the two-lobed leaves (here intermixed with others that are nearly entire), the groups of colourless, unicellular rhizoids and the deeply cleft amphigastria are all features that are readily seen. Each leaf is a single layer of large, nearly isodiametric cells. Archegonia arise apically, a position characteristic of the order as a whole (hence the name Acrogynae), the apical cell being involved in the process. Antheridia occur in the axils of specialized concave leaves just behind the apex and the plants are usually very fertile. A protective envelope (the perianth) surrounds the archegonia and later the developing sporophyte. It is a highly characteristic feature of the order and will be discussed later.

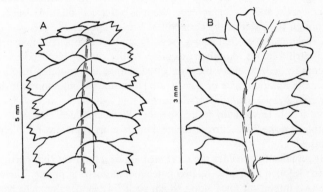

Fig. 5 Leafy shoots viewed from above. A. *Bazzania trilobata*, incubous, and B. *Lophocolea heterophylla*, succubous arrangement of leaves.

Bazzania is best exemplified in Britain by a robust species, *B. trilobata*, which is often abundant in mountain woods in the west and north. The arched, freely branched leafy shoots form conspicuous mats or cushions; and each shoot bears a certain number of nearly bare, descending branches termed flagella. The incubously arranged leaves have three little teeth at their blunt tips; the small amphigastria are multifid. This species is dioecious and only rarely fertile. These two contrasting forms may be used as the foundation on which to build one's knowledge and experience of the host of liverwort genera that like them have adopted a plagiotropous mode of growth with obliquely inserted leaves. We must now consider one or two other variations of leaf arrangement or leaf form that have arisen within the order.

The logical outcome of reduction in size of amphigastria (if indeed reduction has occurred from a once radially symmetrical ancestral form) is the total elimination of these underleaves. Two common British liverworts offering good examples of this are *Plagiochila asplenioides* and *Lophozia ventricosa*. Many Lophoziaceae show amphigastria which have the appearance of being vestigial, for they are minute and confined to positions just behind the growing apex. In the two closely allied mountain genera, *Marsupella* and *Gymnomitrion*, there is no trace of underleaves, although the habit of the commonest British species of *Marsupella*, *M. emarginata*, is often nearly erect. *Bazzania* was noted as unusual in its trifid leaves. Another exception to the rule of bilobed leaves occurs in genera where they are quite simple and rounded in outline, the margin entire or nearly so. Thus, among common British species, *Nardia scalaris*, *Mylia taylori* and *Odontoschisma sphagni* have simple leaves with entire margins; *Plagiochila asplenioides* has simple, markedly decurrent leaves but their margins are minutely toothed.

It remains to consider the most striking development that occurs in the bilobed leaf, with its two independent growing points. There are two important lines along which such further development has taken place, leading to leaves of more complex form than those in the examples cited so far. First, there are plants in which the leaves have become folded, to produce a keel-like form in the basal part of the leaf, whilst distally the smaller antical lobe lies across the large postical lobe. This is seen in *Diplophyllum* and in many species of *Scapania*. Neither genus has any trace of amphigastria. In some species of *Scapania* there is little difference in size between the two lobes. There is a gradual transition to the rather striking shoot pattern of *Diplophyllum* (literally, double leaf) (Fig. 6A).

An even more striking modification occurs when the two growing points of the young leaf remain distinct from the outset, with the result that they develop into two structures almost free from one another and entirely different in form. A good illustration of this is provided by *Frullania*, which is not only one of the largest genera of leafy liverworts, with upwards of 350 species, but is easily obtained in Britain. *Frullania tamarisci* is abundant on rocks and trees in north and west Britain; *F. dilatata* is a generally widespread epiphyte. Either will illustrate the remarkable leaf structure, with the larger, antical lobe expanded and the smaller, postical lobe taking the form of a helmet-shaped pitcher on a short stalk (Fig. 6B). A minute projection, the stylus, grows out from the stalk. It is instructive to examine younger parts of the shoot in *Frullania*, for then stages in the development of the pitchers may be seen. The postical lobe may then appear concave and shell-like in form, but

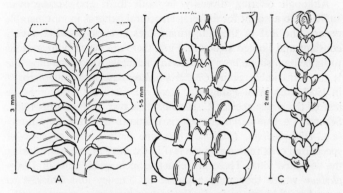

Fig. 6 Further gametophytes of Jungermanniales. A. *Diplophyllum albicans*. B. *Frullania tamarisci*. C. *Lejeunea cavifolia*. (A, dorsal; B and C, ventral views) In each, only small part of leafy stem shown.

far removed from the perfect helmet of maturity. In *Frullania* there is also a row of amphigastria. The ecological significance of these pitchers has been discussed fully by Goebel[85] and by others more recently. Parihar is probably right in suggesting that their main function is to catch water that would be trickling down a tree-trunk or rock face after a shower. In tropical species of *Colura* and *Pleurozia* the postical lobe of each leaf takes the form of a more perfect trap and Müller alludes to its use in trapping minute animals after the fashion of the bladderwort (*Utricularia*). Another tropical genus, *Polyotus*, has helmet-shaped pitchers like those of *Frullania* on both lateral leaves and amphigastria. *Porella*, with five species, has the lobes practically distinct from one another, but the small postical lobe is not saccate. In the enormous family Lejeuneaceae there is a saccate form of postical lobe but it has not become completely separated from the larger, expanded antical lobe (Fig. 6c). As Greig-Smith[88] points out, minute hairs or slime papillae are particularly richly developed on the leaves of Lejeuneaceae, being found in four positions and constituting a valuable taxonomic character in an exceptionally difficult group of genera.

Although offering diversity in both form and arrangement sufficient to account for differing structural patterns in innumerable genera, the leaf of the Jungermanniales is in some ways a very constant and limited structure. First, there are very few exceptions to its being a single layer of cells in thickness. An outstanding one is the remarkable genus *Chondrophyllum* described by Herzog[100] in 1952 from West Patagonia. Here the relatively fleshy concave leaf of the single species *C. cucullatum* is two to three cells thick. Secondly, a true nerve or costa is unknown and it is only rarely (e.g. *Diplophyllum*, *Frullania*) that one finds a row or rows of specialized cells running up the leaf in the median line, constituting the so-called vitta. These are elongate rectangular cells in *Diplophyllum* where they were assumed by Tansley and Chick[228] to serve for conduction. In *Frullania* they are large, rounded cells. When occurring singly or in small groups, they are sometimes called ocelli.

So, too, the rhizoids are subject to little variation. As one would expect, they are numerous in a species such as *Nardia scalaris* which adheres closely to the substratum; and they are very sparse in some erect-growing species such as *Marsupella emarginata*. Often, as in *Lepidozia setacea*, whose slender thread-like stems creep amongst *Sphagnum*, rhizoids are more numerous on older stems. They are almost always colourless, or brownish when old, but are occasionally purple. *Plectocolea obovata* shares this feature with many species of *Fossombronia*, in the Metzgeriales. According to Müller[159], multicellular rhizoids are known only in *Plagiochila paradoxa* and the genus *Schistochila*. Paraphyllia (which are small appendages of varied form) are rarely found; but they clothe the stem of *Trichocolea tomentella*, where they add to the already considerable development of surface and increase the facilities for capillary water travel. The genus *Radula* presents what according to Macvicar[144] is a unique character, namely rhizoids borne directly on the postical lobe of the leaf. One is reminded of the moss *Acrocladium stramineum* where rhizoids not uncommonly spring from leaf tips.

The structure of bryophyte sex organs will be taken up in Chapter 8, but we may now turn to examine that characteristic protective envelope, the perianth. It belongs to the gametophyte generation, although functionally it is associated with the sporophyte. An erect, tubular or funnel-like structure, it is often the most conspicuous feature of small liverworts, such as *Cephalozia* species, when these are fertile. Morphologically, it is sometimes hard to interpret, but taxonomically it has proved very useful.

It is often possible to harmonize the form of the perianth with the idea that it consists of either two or three fully united, modified leaves. Cavers[43] summarized well the four chief arrangements that can result, on this interpretation, and the accompanying diagram (Fig. 7) will make this clear. The four possibilities, with examples, are: (1) three leaves participating, resulting perianth three-angled along lines of union of leaves, e.g. *Lophocolea*; (2) the same, but each leaf folded, resulting perianth three-angled along the median lines or keels of component leaves, e.g. *Cephalozia* and *Frullania*; (3) two leaves participating, not keeled and hence forming a laterally compressed perianth, e.g. *Plagiochila*; (4) the same, but the leaves folded or keeled, hence giving a dorsiventrally compressed perianth, e.g. *Scapania*. Since wherever three leaves participate one is in the mid-ventral line (corresponding with amphigastria) it follows that in type (1) there will be an angle in the median dorsal (or antical) position; in type (2) there will be an angle in the median ventral (or postical) position.

It would be a simple matter if every perianth in the Jungermanniales were referable to one of these four types; but often they take the form of perfectly tubular or lightly creased cylindrical structures which give no hint of an origin from either two or three component leaves. Whatever its correct interpretation, the perianth is very important taxonomically. Macvicar included a statement on perianth as part of his definition of each of the nine 'Sub-families

of the Family Jungermanniaceae Acrogynae' which he recognized
as British. Dealing with the same plants, Jones[119] recognized sixteen
families in the order Jungermanniales and many of these have a
characteristic form of perianth. Often, however, several forms occur
within one family and a perusal of Müller's generic definitions[159]
shows that this structure is even more important at the generic level.

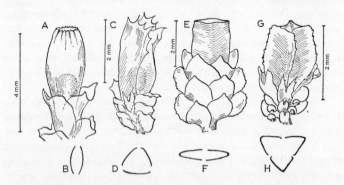

Fig. 7 Perianth structure. Jungermanniales. A. Tubular perianth of
Lophozia ventricosa. B. Plan of laterally compressed, two-member
perianth of *Plagiochila.* C. *Lophocolea heterophylla.* D. Plan of this
three-member perianth. E. *Scapania undulata.* F. Plan of this dorso-
ventrally compressed, two-member perianth. G. *Frullania dilatata.*
H. Plan of this three-member perianth, with folded members and keel
in mid-ventral line.

In a few genera, e.g. *Gymnomitrion*, a perianth is lacking. In
isolated cases elsewhere, e.g. *Trichocolea*, it is replaced functionally
by a remarkable growth of gametophyte stem tissue. The same is
true of *Geocalyx*, *Saccogyna* and *Calypogeia*, in each of which some
form of marsupium is found. This is directly concerned with the
protection and nutrition of the sporophyte and will be taken up in
the next chapter. The perianth itself is relatively late to develop and
ordinarily reaches its full size only when the sporophyte is approaching maturity.

Below the perianth are modified leaves associated with the
archegonia. These are the 'bracts' (corresponding with lateral

leaves) and 'bracteoles' (corresponding with amphigastria). Bracts tend to be larger than vegetative leaves, but in certain cases, e.g. in *Chiloscyphus* and *Calypogeia*, they are smaller. They are often especially reduced in genera that display a marsupial modification of the gametophyte and lack a perianth. At times, as in *Marsupella* and *Plectocolea*, the bracts are fused with the perianth. *Frullania* displays both bracts and bracteole of distinctive form, but with noticeable differences from species to species, and hence useful taxonomically. Where specialized male branches occur they are often catkin-like in form, with their leaves (male bracts) strongly concave to house the antheridia. In such a plant as *Porella platyphylla* (a robust liverwort common in limestone districts) the compact, oblong-ovoid male branch is easily picked out when male plants are worked over under a lens.

Branching in Jungermanniales is never a true dichotomy (forking) brought about by the symmetrical cleavage of an apical cell, although we find apparent dichotomies, e.g. in *Bazzania trilobata*. The systems of branching which occur are complex and varied. They have been fully described and figured by Evans[65]. Terminal branching types, of which four were recognized by Evans, are always intimately related to the mode of origin of derivatives from the three cutting faces of the apical cell. By far the commonest is the *Frullania* type in which the branch comes from the whole ventral half of a lateral segment of the apical cell. This ordinarily produces a leaf of modified form immediately above the point where the branch emerges; in *Frullania* itself it is a leaf which lacks the helmet-shaped postical lobe. The *Radula* type, which occurs also in many Lejeuneaceae, involves no such modification of an associated leaf, since only a small part of the ventral half of a lateral segment takes part in the branch origin. Evans's third (*Microlepidozia*) type is rare. He figured it in *Lepidozia setacea*, but Müller[159] claimed it as characteristic of the related *Telaranea*. Finally, a fourth type is confined to some of the branches in *Acromastigum*. In many leafy liverworts there are also intercalary branches, which arise later, in a ventral or lateral position. Many factors, of course, will contribute to the ultimate habit, or growth-form, achieved (cf. Chapter 10).

Leaf cell dimensions, extent of thickening deposited in the angles of the cells (trigones) and the type of oil body (if any) all provide important taxonomic characters. Among British examples the diameter of the leaf cells varies from 15 μ or less in species of *Cephaloziella* to over 50 μ in *Mylia* and some species of *Cephalozia*. The plate of cells that forms the leaf lacks air-filled intercellular spaces, but large trigones are prominent in many genera, e.g. *Gymnomitrion*, *Mylia*, etc., and it is uncommon for such thickenings to be absent altogether. Oil bodies of varied form, usually somewhat larger than chloroplasts and quite colourless, occur in a high proportion of genera. According to Müller[159] they are usually mixtures, either of terpenes and terpene alcohols or of sesquiterpenes and sesquiterpene alcohols. Their form is often characteristic of particular genera, or even species. Rather little is known of their function.

The young stages of the gametophyte are of interest in the present context mainly in so far as they might throw light on the possible origins of the leafy habit. In recent years Fulford[74], among others, has carried out researches on this subject and has ably summarized the position. There is considerable variation. In a typical case (e.g. *Lophocolea*) a multicellular germ tube grows out from the spore; at the end of this tube or one of its branches a three-dimensional cell mass will arise in which a three-sided apical cell will be cut out. In *Frullania* and many Lejeuneaceae, however, a mass of cells is formed directly on germination, more after the manner of a thalloid liverwort. In this mass arises an apical cell whose derivatives form the leafy shoot system. Long ago Goebel referred to what he called 'reversion to thallus form' among Jungermanniales and if these leafy plants are derived from thalloid ancestors a case of true reversion could be involved. An example which he gave was *Pteropsiella frondiformis*, in which the vegetative plant consists of a band-like thallus; and from this the leafy sexual branches arise. He also cited the minute *Zoopsis argentea*, in which the leaves on the vegetative plant are reduced to a few cells and the assimilatory function is taken over by enlarged cells of the strap-shaped stem. Again the sexual branches bear normal leaves. Of course it would be equally possible to view such examples as stages in a down-grade process involving the gradual loss of leaves and assumption of the thalloid habit by members of the order. It would seem inherently more likely, however, that a juvenile stage should show something of the ancestral form. If so, a filamentous germ tube might be seen as a survival from a remote algal ancestry.

It is doubtful whether many contemporary hepaticologists would concede that an examination of the gametophyte of the Jungermanniales, even in all its stages, could prove much regarding the origin of the group, or even whether they preceded or succeeded thalloid forms. Other lines of evidence would have to be called upon. The fossil record tells us too little to be conclusive (see Chapter 11). The presence within the Jungermanniales of a great number of closely intergrading genera and species, however, is suggestive because it implies that such taxa have not existed long enough to become separated from one another by obvious gaps. It is evidence which cannot readily be thrust aside, for a similar situation prevails elsewhere among groups of organisms that are known to be highly evolved. One has only to think of such families as Compositae and Umbelliferae in the flowering plants.

It remains to consider the Calobryales, which constitute a highly distinct order. In size the order is minute, for it includes only three species of *Calobryum* and one of *Haplomitrium*. *Calobryum* is known from the Far East, South America and the West Indies. *Haplomitrium hookeri* occurs widely in the north temperate region of the Old World and is known from a few localities in North America. It is very rare in Britain.

The two genera differ from all others in that the basal part of the plant consists of a branched, creeping rhizome-like stem, whence arise erect leafy shoots, with their leaves radially disposed. The creeping stem lacks rhizoids. The leaves are simple and entire. Of the three ranks one is sometimes of appreciably smaller size, and this has been equated with the amphigastria of Jungermanniales. Both genera are dioecious and the female plants are acrogynous. Antheridia are in the axils of leaves in *Haplomitrium* but in *Calobryum* they are grouped on a terminal receptacle, surrounded by a cup of enlarged leaves.

Although in the leafy shoots themselves there is a superficial resemblance to radially constructed genera of the Jungermanniales, enough has been noted to show that there are marked differences in many fundamental points of structure. There is no trace, moreover, in *Calobryum* or *Haplomitrium* of the two separate growing points which produce the deeply bifid leaf of such a genus as *Anthelia*. Strangely, the Calobryales combine a rather complex internal anatomy of the gametophyte with a mode of development of the sex organs which has been claimed to be the most primitive found in any bryophyte. Cavers[43], influenced among other things no doubt by the massive calyptra and certain features of the sporophyte, actually grouped the Calobryales with the Anacrogynae (Metzgeriales). Their true affinities remain something of an enigma. It is clear only that they have no really close allies.

Finally, in recent years a very remarkable new liverwort has been discovered in Japan, and since found in western North America. Hattori and Mizutani[95], in discussing its peculiarities, have mentioned that stem branching, some features of cell structure and its apparent lack of dorsi-ventrality are in line with the Calobryales. This puzzling plant has been named *Takakia lepidozioides* and made the basis of a new order, Takakiales. The stems bear groups of linear, cylindrical 'phyllids', usually two or three together (Fig. 3B), and the rather large archegonia are borne terminally in groups. Anything like a final assessment of *Takakia* remains impossible in the absence of sporophytes, but it is suggestive that Hattori and Mizutani quote the noted American hepaticologist, R. M. Schuster, as writing (*in litt.*): 'I am still not sure, but I suspect that a Class parallel with Musci, Hepaticae and Anthocerotae is at hand.' If this were so, the discovery of *Takakia* would be a landmark in the history of bryology.

4

The sporophyte of liverworts

THROUGHOUT the overwhelming majority of liverworts the sporophyte is made up of three components. These are the absorbing and anchoring foot, the stalk-like seta and the capsule which contains typically spores and elaters. Müller, like some others, uses the term sporogonium to refer to the capsule alone. In this text it is used in its wider meaning, when it becomes practically synonymous with the sporophyte. In a few liverworts, such as *Riccia*, the sporophyte is of a much simpler construction, whilst in *Anthoceros* it is different again in many important respects. Due consideration will be given to these two at a later point. More typical examples may be found in the Sphaerocarpales, Marchantiales, Calobryales, Metzgeriales and Jungermanniales. The sporophyte, small and compact by comparison with the thalloid or leafy gametophyte, has often been considered as wholly parasitic. This is not completely true since chloroplasts occur freely in the capsule wall cells, commonly in the outermost two or three cell layers of the seta and occasionally (according to Müller, in *Sphaerocarpos*) in the foot.

The foot varies much in size and shape. Its width commonly exceeds that of the seta, so that it forms the swollen base of the sporophyte. It must surely serve as the principal pathway for absorption of nutrients from the gametophyte, although there is little experimental work to support this idea. The organ is nearly globose in many Marchantiales, including forms like *Corsinia* which lack a carpocephalum and others like *Reboulia* and *Conocephalum* which have one. In Metzgeriales and Jungermanniales it is often anchor-shaped in longitudinal section and the dagger-like apex may penetrate far into gametophyte tissue (Fig. 8D). Both *Sphaerocarpos* and *Monocarpus* have the foot quite well developed.

47

On the other hand in some advanced Jungermanniales, e.g. *Lejeunea*, it is remarkably small.

The very young seta is composed of transversely elongated cells. The ultimate elongation of these cells in *Pellia* is said to proceed at a rate of 1 mm per hour and they may achieve individual lengths of 700 to 900 μ. A long seta is usual in Metzgeriales and Jungermanniales, even if few genera attain the great lengths (*c.* 5 cm) seen

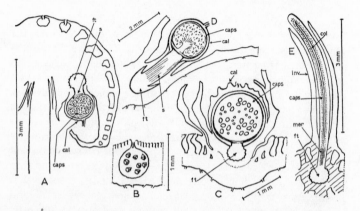

Fig. 8 Longitudinal sections of some liverwort sporophytes compared. A. Part of carpocephalum of *Reboulia hemisphaerica* in longitudinal section, with pendent sporophyte. B. *Riccia* sp. spore tetrads lying free in old archegonial venter. C. *Corsinia* sp. D. *Pellia epiphylla*. E. *Anthoceros* sp. young. cal. calyptra; caps. capsule; col. columella; ft. foot; inv. involucre; mer. meristem; s. seta.

in *Pellia*. Among Marchantiales, *Monoclea* is exceptional in having a long seta (Fig. 3D). Obviously the value of a long seta is lost when that organ does not elevate the spore-container, but merely brings it nearer to the ground. This is what happens in the pendent sporogonia of Marchantiales with carpocephala, and the role of the seta is then discharged when it has carried the capsule clear of the 'head' itself and any attendant enveloping structures. Perhaps it is significant that even in *Targionia* and *Corsinia*, where no carpocephalum is formed, the seta is still short. The seta of liverworts is always a delicate and (after lengthening) an ephemeral structure; it is always nearly colourless at maturity and composed mainly of thin-walled cells. In the precise arrangement of these cells in a transverse section of the seta Müller[159] has seen a useful taxonomic character. For example, in *Cephaloziella* only four cells compose the transverse section; whilst in *Cephalozia* four central cells are surrounded by a ring of eight much larger ones.

The capsule varies from narrowly ovoid to sub-spherical in shape (Fig. 10), appearing dark in colour with a glossy surface. The dark colour it owes to its densely packed contents; the gloss is imparted by a kind of cuticle, for it is important that there should not be excessive loss of water through the capsule wall before dehiscence. The variation in shape is of some taxonomic significance. Thus, the capsule is much more nearly ovoid-cylindrical in *Riccardia* and *Blasia* than it is in *Pellia* and *Fossombronia*, where it is nearly globose. In the Jungermanniales (leafy liverworts) narrowly ovoid capsules are common, but the globose form is found in *Frullania* and its allies. The name *Sphaerocarpos* alludes to the nearly spherical capsule. Other aberrant genera, for example *Monoclea* in the Marchantiales, *Haplomitrium* and *Calobryum* in the Calobryales, have markedly elongated capsules. Liverwort capsules tend to be small compared with those of some mosses. One might expect capsules of carpocephalous Marchantiales (where several commonly hang from one 'umbrella') to be among the smallest, but this does not appear to be so. In fact, a capsule diameter of 1 to 1·25 mm prevails among these, whereas figures as low as 0·5 to 0·6 mm are found among Jungermanniales. A diameter of 1·5 mm may be found in *Pellia* and *Riccardia* in the Metzgeriales.

Ordinarily, the ripe capsule contains only spores and free elaters. An elaterophore, which bears fixed elaters, occurs at the base of the capsule in *Pellia*, at the apex in *Riccardia*. O'Hanlon[169] noted that in *Marchantia polymorpha* one elater was produced for every 128 spores. As Müller points out, the disparity is seldom so great as this. The elaters, long, narrow cells with single or double (occasionally multiple) spirals of thickening on the inside of the cell wall, are highly characteristic of liverworts. Also, as we shall see, they are highly efficient, in several different ways. In *Sphaerocarpos* and its ally *Riella*, in *Monocarpus* and again in *Corsinia*, no elaters are found and the spores are associated with rounded sterile cells which appear to have a nutritive function. These are the equivalent of sterilized spore mother cells, not modified elaters. An elater is normally formed from the equivalent of a row of spore mother cells.

The wall of the capsule is one layer of cells thick in the Marchantiales, two to several layers in Metzgeriales and Jungermanniales. Characteristic bands of thickening run anticlinally across the wall cells in Marchantiales, and across the cells of one or more of the layers in the others. In *Lophocolea*, for example, the capsule wall consists of several cell layers, with thickenings in all of them, although the outermost layer has the largest and most heavily thickened cells. The number of cell layers and distribution of thickenings is often characteristic of a genus, or a whole family. The thickenings are important in dehiscence, which normally occurs by splitting into four valves.

In *Pellia* the capsule splits to the base, from which arises the tuft of fixed elaters. In the related *Riccardia* fixed elaters stand more or less erect near the tip of each valve after dehiscence (Fig. 10D). Other arrangements exist in the four-valved capsules of *Lophocolea* and *Frullania*. In some Jungermanniales, e.g. *Lejeunea*, *Frullania*, the split does not extend to the base of the capsule. *Cryptothallus* (Metzgeriales), very unusual in its four valves failing to separate distally, has been mentioned earlier (p. 25). Capsules of the old group 'Operculatae' of the Marchantiales (*Plagiochasma*, *Reboulia* and *Grimaldia*) shed a definite 'operculum' or lid, leaving the open capsule in the form of a neat urn. In most other Marchantiales with a carpocephalum the capsule breaks up irregularly when mature. Nor is there any definite mode of dehiscence in *Corsinia*. *Sphaerocarpos* and *Riella* are described by Müller as cleistocarpous (i.e. with no true dehiscence). We shall see later that *Riccia* too is cleistocarpous but the wall of the simple capsule disappears early and the surrounding gametophyte tissue ultimately breaks down to release the spores.

The spores of liverworts vary enormously both in size and in output per capsule. As might be expected, to some extent these figures vary inversely. Thus, only about 200 of the massive tetrads of *Sphaerocarpos* are formed in one capsule. According to Jack[115] some 4,500 of the very large spores of *Pellia epiphylla* occur in one capsule. Müller[159] gives figures ranging from 2,000 to 8,000 spores per capsule for various genera of the higher (carpocephalous) Marchantiales. All these outputs are low compared with the figures attributed by him to some members of the leafy Jungermanniales. It is easier to credit the figure of about 24,000 cited for *Lophocolea cuspidata* than the estimated 400,000 for *Diplophyllum albicans* and 1,000,000 for *Scapania undulata*. These are high figures, even allowing for the small size of some spores in the Jungermanniales (some have a diameter less than one-twentieth that of the larger spores in the Marchantiales). In spite of a relatively modest output per capsule, the great fecundity of a plant such as *Marchantia polymorpha*, where many capsules arise in each of the numerous carpocephala, enables a single well-grown gametophyte to account for a prodigious spore production. O'Hanlon[169] estimated the figure of *c.* 7,000,000 from one plant (twenty-four capsules, each with 300,000). Precocious germination of spores is usual in *Pellia*, where they are often multicellular long before the seta has lengthened. This feature is also found in *Porella*, *Radula* and certain other genera.

The sporophyte in the great majority of liverworts is thus a structure remarkably constant in its main components, less so as regards their finer details. In such details one sometimes sees significant differences; for example in the different arrangements of cells in the transverse sections of setae, or the precise structure of different capsule walls; or again in spore size, elater structure, or ratio of spore to elater numbers. These various characters of the mature sporophyte provide much of systematic value, to be considered alongside gametophyte structure in assessing relationships. Superficially gametophytes are so much more diverse that one always thinks first of their characters when separating genera or families. A clear-cut difference, however, between two sporophytes could well be of great significance, for the liverwort sporophyte on the whole is a conservative structure. Thus, the difference between unistratose and multistratose capsule walls may well point to an ancient and fundamental cleavage between the two groups concerned.

Before we turn to two interesting aberrant cases, *Riccia* and *Anthoceros*, three general topics call for discussion. These are (1) embryology and early development; (2) protection and nutrition of the sporophyte; (3) spore discharge. The first played a big part in the older morphologists' discussions, but after some sixty years of intensive effort it was realized that embryological investigation was less rewarding than had been hoped. The lead had come from zoologists who from early times had been accustomed to draw on embryology for much significant evidence. Perhaps such evidence is to be found more readily in the unfolding of the complex organs and tissue systems of a highly organized animal than in the comparatively simple structure of a liverwort sporophyte. Nevertheless, two discoveries of some value were made. The first indicated that the early embryo either (1) passed through the octant stage (ball of eight cells) or (2) passed instead through a linear stage consisting of a chain of four cells (tiered embryo). The second discovery concerned a later stage, namely the origin of the sporogenous tissue. After the first periclinal walls have appeared it is evident that the forerunners of spore mother cells (archesporium) can be cut out either internal to or external to these walls. Putting the matter another way, we can describe the sporogenous tissue as referable to endothecium, or amphithecium. These two considerations were formerly judged of paramount importance and they weighed heavily with Cavers[43] in his very thorough discussion of the interrelationships of the Bryophyta. One hears much less of them today. Müller however, with long experience behind him, was careful to stress the importance of sporophyte characters in general, and those of development in particular.

The difficulty about early embryology in the present context lies in the fact that, whereas an octant stage is typical of Marchantiales and a linear stage typical of Jungermanniales, within the single close-knit group of the carpocephalous Marchantiales we find both represented. With *Conocephalum* showing the tiered, *Marchantia* the octant, arrangement of cells in the early embryo, it is difficult to regard such a difference as fundamental. The second criterion can be even less helpful since all liverworts except the Anthocerotales form their sporogenous tissue from the endothecium. We shall see that in some Anthocerotales the position is equivocal.

Adequate protection and nutrition are very important for the success of the sporophyte and it is interesting to enquire how these are achieved in different instances. In such widely separated genera as *Sphaerocarpos*, *Corsinia*, *Targionia* and *Pellia* a similar general situation prevails. The green thalloid gametophyte houses the foot in each case and from its own resources provides for the adequate nutrition of the whole sporophyte. In all typical instances immediate protection for the sporophyte is provided by the calyptra, an enlargement of archegonial venter tissue; but external to this, each genus cited has its own additional protective structures. *Sphaerocarpos* has the prominent pear-shaped involucres which cover much of the thallus; *Corsinia* has a green curtain of tissue which arises late among the archegonia and which some have seen as the forerunner of a carpocephalum. The paired purplish black scales which enfold the sporophyte provide the characteristic involucre of *Targionia*, whilst in *Pellia* we meet with green involucres that are flap-like or collar-shaped according to the species. *Riccardia*, different again, has a particularly massive calyptra (six to eight cells thick), and lacks additional protection.

Quite another situation obtains in the carpocephalous Marchantiales, where the foot is embedded, not in thallus tissue, but in the substance of the mushroom-like head that forms the body of the carpocephalum. One notes that in the massive, rich green heads of *Reboulia hemisphaerica* (Fig. 8A) there is not only ample provision for photosynthesis (air chambers, green cells and barrel-shaped pores) but there is abundant storage tissue. Thus in the well-developed carpocephalum the inverted sporophytes are firmly embedded and well supplied. Additional protection external to the calyptra varies from genus to genus, often consisting of diaphanous sheaths of tissue. *Marchantia* represents the extreme case, with calyptra, perianth and involucre. *Fimbriaria*, allied to *Reboulia*, shows like *Marchantia* an individual perianth around each archegonium; and this perianth, becoming laciniate into four to sixteen strips, looks like a Chinese lantern around the mature sporophyte.

Sometimes the strips remain coherent at their tips and the spores are shed through the slits so formed.

The Jungermanniales, bearing their archegonia at the tips of slender leafy shoots, would seem less favourably constructed for the protection of the ensuing sporophyte. Almost all, however, have the tubular or funnel-shaped perianth that has been described in Chapter 3. It is possibly significant that this structure should be lacking in the genus *Gymnomitrion*, where the species are mainly inhabitants of high alpine and arctic regions. For prolonged winter snow lie will provide the necessary protection and the capsule can emerge in spring to shed its spores between June and August. By far the most interesting development to be found in the Jungermanniales, in this context, is the marsupium. In its typical form this is a pouch-like accretion of gametophyte origin which results in a profound change in the region of the sporophyte insertion. Just as the calyptra implies a potentiality of further growth in the tissue of the archegonial venter, so a marsupium implies such a potentiality in a certain part of the stem itself.

The different kinds of marsupium* have never been more clearly set forth than they were by Cavers[43], who also pointed out that a full marsupial development was often correlated with a loss of true calyptra, or perianth, or both. Two main types occur, but there are many variants. In the first a rapid, localized growth of gametophyte stem tissue takes place on the same axis as that of the leafy shoot itself. This, exemplified by *Trichocolea*, results in no striking tuber-like outgrowth but rather in the total replacement of true calyptra by proliferating stem tissue (Fig. 9D). In *Trichocolea* the stout sheath so formed betrays its origin by the leaves which it bears and by the involucral bracts which crown it. In the parallel case of *Isotachis* there is a rapid upward growth of stem tissue in the region immediately beneath the archegonia. The sheath-like marsupium in effect replaces a perianth and the sporophyte is surrounded by a true calyptra in the usual way. Penetration of the anchor-shaped foot into stem tissue is deeper in *Trichocolea* than in *Isotachis*.

The second and more noticeable type of marsupium forms a

* See also Knapp, E. in Bot. Abhandl. K. Goebel, Heft 16, Gustav Fischer, Jena, 1930.

tuber-like outgrowth of stem tissue ventrally, i.e. at a right angle
with the creeping axis of the leafy shoot. Down into this the long
foot grows, to be embedded deeply in a pendulous, fleshy mass of
gametophyte tissue. This is plentifully equipped with rhizoids and
with storage capacity. It is effectively roofed over by overlapping
leaves and its interior surface is lined with mucilage hairs. It occurs
incipiently in *Nardia geoscyphus* (Fig. 9c); in its fully developed

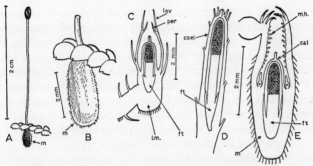

Fig. 9 A. *Calypogeia* sp. Part of leafy shoot, with sporophyte and
conspicuous marsupium. B. Enlarged view of the massive, pendulous
marsupium. C–E. Diagrammatic longitudinal sections of 3 sporophytes to show different types of marsupial structure (re-drawn from
Cavers). C. *Nardia geoscyphus* type. D. A type found in the genus
Trichocolea. E. *Calypogeia* type (at younger stage than A–B) cal.
calyptra; coel. 'coelocaul'—formed of stem tissue—and a kind of
marsupial structure, although loosely called calyptra in descriptive
works; ft. foot; i.m. incipient marsupium; inv. involucre; m. marsupium; m.h. mucilage hairs; per. perianth. In C–E the capsule is
shown dark.

form in *Geocalyx*, *Saccogyna* and *Calypogeia* (Fig. 9). Although a
calyptra persists here, a perianth is rendered completely superfluous.
Altogether, a pendulous marsupium of this kind represents the
most perfect development to be found among liverworts for the
protection and nutrition of the sporophyte.

It is not intended to dwell at length on capsule ripening, with its
attendant processes of tetrad division in the spore mother cells,
elater maturation and deposition of thickenings in the ripening
capsule wall. Dehiscence of the capsule too has already been

considered in a general way, and we may turn now to examine in some detail a few representative methods of spore discharge. We are fortunate in having available Ingold's extremely clear and thorough exposition on this subject[111], and it should be consulted by everyone interested in the precise role of the elaters in different examples. Following up the earlier observations of Kamerling[122] and amplifying them with his own, Ingold recognizes three distinct mechanisms effecting spore discharge among liverworts. These are (1) the water rupture mechanism, seen in *Cephalozia*, *Lophocolea* and most leafy liverworts; (2) the hygroscopic mechanism, seen in *Marchantia* and indeed most members of the Marchantiales with elaters, also in *Pellia* and other Metzgeriales; (3) the spiral-spring mechanism which appears to be peculiar to the Frullaniaceae and Lejeuneaceae. The first and the third are violent methods, the second much less so. In all of them the elaters are the operative structures, together with the opening valves of the capsule wall. The essential feature of *Cephalozia*, and liverworts like it, lies in the great strength of the bi-spiral thickening on the inside wall of the clear, water-filled elater (Fig. 10H). On exposure to dry air this double spiral band contracts sharply, bringing the contained water under severe tension. Finally, the tendency of the spiral to revert to its original shape is too strong for the cohesive power of the reduced water content of the elater; the water 'breaks' and a gas phase takes its place. Instantaneously, the elater untwists and, as Ingold graphically describes it, this 'tears the elater free from the sporangium wall, hurls it still rotating into the air, and flings off the attached spores'.

By comparison, the single spiral band in each elater of *Marchantia* and the double band in *Pellia* are much weaker. Here the spirals never reach a stage, on withdrawal of water from the elater, when the strength of their tendency to untwist is sufficient to induce water rupture. As a result, they perform only comparatively feeble twisting or 'wriggling' movements in response to changes in atmospheric humidity. By such movements, of course, it is possible to 'fluff up' the mass of spores and facilitate their gradual dispersal.

The unique arrangement in Frullaniaceae and Lejeuneaceae depends upon their having a series of elaters extending from the roof to the floor of the globose capsule, and firmly attached at both ends. Hence, as the four valves of the capsule bend back in dehiscence, there is a fraction of a second when each elater is drawn out so that its single band of thickening forms a stretched spiral spring in a water-filled tube. Ingold emphasizes that this stage is passed through rapidly, for in less than a second after the onset of capsule

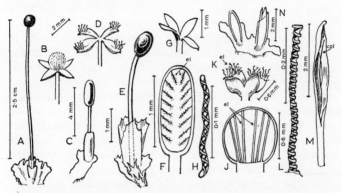

Fig. 10 Dehiscence of capsule and spore discharge in liverworts. A–B. *Pellia epiphylla*, capsules before and after dehiscence. C–D. *Riccardia pinguis*, the same. E–H. *Lophocolea heterophylla*. E. Capsule, seta and perianth. F. L.S. intact capsule, diagrammatic (after Ingold). G. Old, empty capsule. H. Elater; note double spiral. J–L. *Frullania dilatata*. J. L.S. intact capsule, diagrammatic (after Ingold). K. Old capsule, after spore discharge. L. Elater; note single spiral. M. *Anthoceros* sp. Distal part of capsule in dehiscence. N. *Notothylas orbicularis*, part of thallus with two capsules, one beginning to open. col. columella; el. elaters.

opening all the elaters will have been torn free at their lower ends. Quickly the base of each elater moves out in an arc until a series of elaters—their original shape resumed—stand more or less erect on each of the four expanded valves of the capsule wall (Fig. 10, J, K, L). Spore discharge is effected by this rapid upward and outward movement of the freed bases of the elaters. Any subsequent movement that they perform, light twisting induced by further drying, is unimportant. This unique method, it will be observed, is associated with a unique internal organization of the capsule. That fact did not escape the attention of the earlier observers who also noted that in these families the splitting of the capsule wall into four valves only extends for two-thirds of its length, leaving the basal third as an intact bowl. Spruce[220] attached such importance to these features that he divided the whole range of liverworts, which compose the modern Metzgeriales and Jungermanniales, into two groups, one containing *Frullania*, *Lejeunea* and their immediate allies, the other all the rest.

So far this chapter has been descriptive rather than phyletic in its approach. One reason is that two very important links in any phyletic series remain to be considered. Each is very different from any hepatic sporophyte so far examined. Of the two, *Riccia* and *Anthoceros*, the former will be described first. It stands apart because it is the simplest known sporophyte structure among bryophytes. In all species of *Riccia* a capsule alone exists, there being no trace of seta or foot. At an early stage the archegonial venter will have become two-layered by periclinal divisions, whilst the nearly spherical capsule consists of a single-layered wall and the enclosed mass of sporogenous tissue. Sometimes certain cells of this mass fail to form spores; such sterile cells, or 'nurse cells' (from their undoubted nutritive function), were detected by Pagan[170] in *R. crystallina*. At maturity the capsule wall ('jacket layer' of Smith[218]) breaks down to a variable extent. As the inner layer of the old archegonial venter commonly breaks down too, the spores will ultimately lie free in a delicate sac formed only of the outer layer of the venter (Fig. 8B). As Smith points out, we have the anomaly of the so-called sporophyte of *Riccia* at this stage consisting of a sac provided by an earlier gametophyte housing spores that represent the new gametophyte—and no diploid tissue at all! Spore dispersal awaits the break-up of the surrounding thallus tissue, but this does not mean, of course, the death of the plant. As the apices continue to cut off new cells and the dichotomizing thallus pushes forward, so the surface of older, darker green parts becomes erumpent and the large black spores escape. Fortunately, *Riccia glauca* and *R. sorocarpa* are both fairly common plants in Britain and if one examines their neat rosettes one can often see the new growth fresh and vivid green, the older parts duller, pitted with sporophyte hollows and spattered with loose spores.

The embryology of *Riccia* seems to be of little significance since both tiered and octant types are known within the genus. *Oxymitra*, closely allied to *Riccia*, to a large extent shares its simplicity of sporophyte, although it is normal here for a number of sterile cells to occur within the capsule. So far as sporophyte structure is concerned, neither genus of the family Ricciaceae helps much to bridge the gap between them and other Marchantiales. Lack of foot and seta effectively sets them apart.

As is well known, Bower[23] seized upon the extraordinarily simplified sporophyte of *Riccia* as the natural starting point in the evolution of land plants through a process of sterilization of more and more 'potentially sporogenous tissue'. Seen in this way, as the base-line of his antithetic theory of the origin of land plants from algal ancestors, *Riccia* acquires great importance morphologically; and from it can be traced a beautiful ascending series through *Corsinia* to the higher Marchantiales. Cavers[43] accepted without question the validity of such an ascending series. Many bryologists today, however, would regard the very simple sporophyte of *Riccia* as the product of reduction. Müller and Evans are two of great eminence who in recent years have shared this view.

The sporophyte of *Anthoceros* is of the greatest interest, and its many unusual features have given support to the argument for raising the order Anthocerotales to the rank of a sub-class equated with mosses and hepatics. This is what Smith, following Howe[108], has done in his Anthocerotae; so too Parihar[173] in his Anthocerotopsida. The view taken here is that such a step is perhaps not necessary, although *Anthoceros* remains a very remarkable plant.

It will be helpful to summarize the most important features of the sporophyte, and then elaborate on some of them. Thus, (1) there is no seta, only a massive foot and a long, cylindrical capsule; (2) the capsule grows for a long period, from a basal intercalary meristem (Fig. 8E); (3) there is elaborate internal organization into central columella, elongate but domed sporogenous tissue of amphithecial origin, and wall composed of several layers of green cells and an epidermis with stomata; (4) dehiscence is by two (at times more) valves, the rupture extending downwards from near the apex, thus continually exposing spores of more and more recent origin. The spores are intermixed with 'pseudo-elaters' which, despite lack of spiral thickenings, perform some hygroscopic movements which aid in dispersal. Proskauer[186] has given a very thorough account of this and the associated spiralling of the dried-out valves.

It is plain that the long-growing capsule, the massive foot and the complex internal organization, with photosynthetic power unmatched elsewhere among liverwort sporophytes, combine to give this unique structure almost all that it needs to become free-living. Normally, however, the foot is firmly anchored in gameto-phyte tissue; and the slender light green capsules, which remind one of the seedling shoots of a fine-leaved grass, are semi-parasitic. Many years ago, Campbell[36] placed on record an isolated instance of this sporophyte achieving something more. He found unusually large plants of the Californian *Anthoceros fusiformis* which had grown for nine months. They were on the brink of achieving independence from the ageing gametophyte. Some parts near the base of the capsule had ceased to produce spores almost completely, and there were corresponding increases in the extent of photo-synthetic tissue, in size of obviously conducting columella and massive, absorbing foot.

Campbell's specimens came nearer to full independence than anything ever seen in a bryophyte sporogonium before. In this connection some have thought of the Psilophytales, but we must remember that the sporophyte of *Anthoceros* not only has no roots; it has no vascular tissue in the true sense and no branching; more-over, the meristem is at the base, not the apex of the 'shoot'.

It is true that those features which were emphasized in Campbell's unusual specimens are among the most remarkable that *Anthoceros* offers. I refer to the long-lived meristem, the photosynthetic capsule wall and the tenuous columella which usually appears as a plate of sixteen cells in transverse sections of the capsule. But the capsule is also exceptional among hepatics in its long, narrow shape, its stomata, and the curious, one- to three-celled pseudo-elaters. More-over, the mode of dehiscence is unique (Fig. 10M), the development of sporogenous tissue from amphithecium is without parallel in liverworts, and the large chloroplasts (usually two per cell) are unlike those of other bryophytes. This is a formidable catalogue and would suffice to accord *Anthoceros* unique status if it had no close relatives, nor intermediates between itself and normal liverwort sporophytes. However, it does not stand alone, and apart from 'splits' off the large genus *Anthoceros* itself (*Aspiromitus*, *Phaeoceros*) there are the important genera *Notothylas*, *Dendroceros* and *Megaceros*, all of which are indisputably linked with *Anthoceros* on the evidence of strong gametophyte resemblances. The first, *Notothylas*, is the most important in the present context.

The short capsules of *Notothylas orbicularis* (only *c.* 2 mm long) grow out nearly horizontally from the fertile branches of the rosette (Fig. 10N) and seem remarkably unlike those of *Anthoceros* species. Not only are they short and compact, but chlorophyll is almost absent and there are no stomata. Early investigators noted the variable extent of a sterile columella, which in some species appeared to be totally lacking, so that the whole endothecium formed spores and elaters. Lang[129], in a careful and thorough study of *N. breutelii*, found that the central products of the basal meristem at first formed sporogenous tissue but later in the life of the capsule gave rise to sterile cells which could result in a short columella being present in the mature capsule. He also demonstrated that in the embryology of the sporophyte *Notothylas* was perfectly in line with the prevailing pattern of the Anthocerotales. More recently Kashyap and Dutt[123] and Pandé[171-2] have studied Indian species of the genus and confirmed that the columella is highly variable from species to species. Elaters in *Notothylas* commonly have at least rudimentary rings or spirals and dehiscence is usually by the imperfect separation of two broad valves, from the apex downwards. Pandé cites species, however, in which the opening is follicular, along one suture only.

Notothylas at once appears as a link between *Anthoceros* and more normal liverworts; for it is evident that many of the most arresting sporophyte characters of *Anthoceros* are either lacking or present in modified form here. Cavers[43] clearly regarded it as more primitive than *Anthoceros* and even went so far as to name

Anthoceros hallii as a link (in the upward march of events) between the two genera. It is interesting that in 1907 Lang had put forward the opposite view, that *Notothylas* was a reduced member of the Anthocerotales that had largely lost its columella. If one agrees with Lang in this one can continue to regard the sporophyte of *Notothylas* as a 'link' with those of ordinary liverworts only if one begins the series with *Anthoceros* and regards Jungermanniales and Metzgeriales as examples of still further reduction. In my view, this involves considerable difficulties.

In current morphological literature one finds in fact two diametrically opposed views regarding *Anthoceros*. The one, chiefly favoured by the older morphologists, holds that its sporophyte at least is advanced and specialized; the other (a view widely held today) claims that the sporophyte of *Anthoceros* is an archaic survival. Those who hold this second view believe that bryophytes sprang from ancestors in which sporophyte and gametophyte generations were more or less alike, both being green and radially symmetrical. Since the sporophyte of *Anthoceros* is the only known liverwort sporophyte which is a long, green cylindrical structure it is, on this view, regarded as the closest living approach to the lost ancestry. This homologous theory of bryophyte origin (cf. Fulford[71]), once accepted, is bound to affect one's views not only on *Anthoceros*, but on the arrangement and phyletic significance of all groups of liverworts.

5

Gametophyte of mosses

THE branched, filamentous protonema which forms on spore germination is invariably succeeded by a leafy shoot system or gametophore. In some mosses, for example *Sphagnum* and *Andreaea*, the forerunner of the leafy shoots is a plate of cells. The leafy shoots present a great diversity of gross form, and of fine structure, in the different families and genera of mosses. They offer many taxonomic characters of importance; yet the gametophyte has not been much called upon to provide evidence regarding moss evolution. There exists for mosses no modern review of interrelationships comparable with those of Campbell[37], Evans[66] and Fulford[71] for hepatics, in which the gametophyte could have received due weight in the discussion. This is not wholly surprising because for all its diversity the gametophyte of mosses shows an underlying uniformity of plan. Moreover, the existing differences are in the main of a kind to be accorded only minor importance in an evolutionary context.

With very few exceptions the leafy shoot grows by means of a tetrahedral apical cell, in the form of an inverted pyramid with three cutting faces. Even in such a case as *Fissidens*, where the apical cell is characteristically two-sided rather than three-sided, that in the youngest shoots has the normal three cutting faces. In all ordinary examples it follows therefore that the resulting stem bears leaves whose basic arrangement is in three ranks. Owing to growth torsions and consequent displacement, this precise arrangement is soon lost in most instances. *Fontinalis*, however, continues to display the strictly three ranked leaf arrangement. If the naturally twisted ('rope-like') shoots of *Grimmia funalis* be 'unwound' by hand the underlying three-ranked leaf arrangement is again plain. In mature shoots of *Fissidens* species the leaves are strictly in two

63

ranks. The apparent five-ranked leaf formation of some species of *Sphagnum* (e.g. *S. quinquefarium*) is secondarily acquired, and the normal three-sided apical cell prevails in this genus too. Thus, stem and leaves, or cauloid and phylloids as some[124] would call them, are two of the fundamental organs of the moss gametophore. The third is the rhizoid system. This closely resembles protonema in structure and is developed to a varying extent.

Much of the characteristic appearance of particular mosses is imparted by their branching system. Ruhland[201] has indicated the manner of formation of branches. Unlike higher plants, many mosses form branches just below leaves rather than in their axils. The branch originates by a cell belonging to the surface layer of the stem becoming secondarily specialized as a new apical. It then proceeds to function like the original apical cell. If growth of the branch is rapid one may gain the impression of dichotomy (forking). If many new apicals arise regularly on opposite sides of the stem, each initiating a lateral of limited growth, a pinnate or 'plumose' type of shoot will result, such as one sees in *Ctenidium molluscum*, or even more strikingly in the boreal forest moss, *Ptilium crista-castrensis*. Thus, the frequency of new initials, together with the direction of growth of both main stem and lateral branches, will largely determine the 'habit' of a particular species. Where a main stem grows erect for several centimetres, bearing laterals only in the form of a subterminal crown of branches, a 'miniature tree' (or dendroid habit) results. This is well seen in *Climacium dendroides* (Fig. 19J) (found by lake margins and in dune 'slacks'), and to a lesser extent in *Thamnium alopecurum* (limestone woods and boulders in mountain ravines). Hörmann[106] has recently prepared a careful account of the structure of these two dendroid mosses. We return to this topic in Chapter 10.

It will be well to examine at this stage the purely vegetative gametophyte structure in selected examples from each of the principal sub-classes (Reimers—see Chapter 1) of mosses. The following will be considered:

Sphagnidae	*Sphagnum*
Andreaeidae	*Andreaea*

Bryidae   *Funaria, Hypnum*
Buxbaumiidae   *Buxbaumia*
Polytrichidae   *Polytrichum*

This will serve to display the salient lines of specialization in the leafy shoot in so far as these are exemplified by major taxonomic groups. Descriptions of these examples are available in many textbooks and it will suffice to mention their principal features. *Sphagnum* offers the greatest number of unique features, and it will be considered first.

The genus *Sphagnum* is very large, with over 300 species, distributed in almost every part of the world. They are known as bog mosses, and they make these wet habitats increasingly acid by their activity. On the erect-growing stems the branches arise in fascicles, often five together (Fig. 19D). Commonly some will grow out laterally, whilst others of the fascicle are 'descending branches' and hang down very close to the main stem. The branches near the apex are usually shorter, stouter and crowded. They compose the so-called comal tuft, but as new growth appears these in turn will be displaced downwards.

The main stem is comparatively stout (diameter up to 1·2 mm) and shows well marked differentiation of tissues (see Chapter 9 and Fig. 18G). The leaves on it are usually different in shape, size and details of cell structure from those on the branches. It is worth while to dissect out some young leaves from a bud of *Sphagnum* to see the regular manner in which cell division proceeds, with its resulting pattern of alternating living green cells and clear, hyaline, water-filled cells with ring-like thickenings. This has often been figured[43,173,218], and requires emphasis here only because it is an arrangement of cells that sets *Sphagnum* apart from all other mosses (cf. Chapter 11). There is no midrib. Mature plants are without rhizoids. Rigidity is not required of the *Sphagnum* stem, for in all except submerged aquatics the stems grow in the dense clumps familiar to everyone who walks much in bog and moorland country. Except in dry weather, these clumps are charged with water (numerous holes providing direct entry to the hyaline leaf cells); and the plants glow with many bright colours—deep red in *S. rubellum*, salmon to rose-pink in *S. plumulosum*, orange-brown and various shades of green or yellow in others. Paton and Goodman[177] found that the pigment responsible for the rose-red colour was an anthocyanin very firmly held in the cell walls.

Much has been written on the capacity of *Sphagnum* to increase the acidity of its environment by a process of selective ionic absorption[217] and Rose[200] has shown that the pH in the interior of the tufts is often markedly lower (e.g. 4·4 against 6·0) than in the surrounding aqueous medium. This is a particularly marked case of a property apparently shared by other plants with comparable cell walls; but in many structural features of the gametophyte *Sphagnum* stands apart; and we have yet to consider sex organs and sporophyte which will provide further evidence of isolation. Thus, it is not easy to concede to Gams' recent plea[77] that *Sphagnum* be viewed as a 'reduced' evolutionary line, derived from Leucobryoid ancestry. *Leucobryum* is an important genus of the order Dicranales in the Bryidae, which shares with *Sphagnum* the capacity to store water in certain dead, hyaline cells of the leaf. It is difficult to see that it shares much else. Even this leaf (with a layer of green cells sandwiched between two layers of hyaline cells) is fundamentally unlike that of *Sphagnum* (cf. Fig. 18).

The small, blackish-green or olive-brown tufts of *Andreaea* present few features of the leafy shoot to set them apart from many Bryidae. Goebel[85] alluded to a fundamentally primitive mode of segmentation in the leaf of *Andreaea*, however. The relative isolation of the genus is based on characters derived from sporophyte, sex organs and prothallus, probably in that order of importance. Such a plant as *Andreaea rupestris* looks not unlike small states of *Rhacomitrium heterostichum* var. *gracilescens*, which may be growing on the same siliceous mountain rocks.

The stems are slender and short, with apparent dichotomies. The leaves vary in shape with the species; they may be nerved or not. The most unusual features of the haploid generation seem to be the plate-like protonema (which makes for firm anchorage on the hard rock) and the gametophyte stalk, or 'pseudopodium' which lifts the capsule clear of the perichaetial leaves. Functionally it replaces the seta.

Among Bryidae, our two examples offer many contrasts. *Funaria* illustrates the erect, little-branched 'acrocarp' habit; *Hypnum cupressiforme* the prostrate, freely branched, 'pleurocarp' habit. The leaves in *F. hygrometrica* are large, oblong-ovate and shortly acute at the apex, with large cells of rectangular or hexagonal-rectangular outline in surface view. The leaves in *H. cupressiforme* are strongly curved, finely acuminate, with long narrow cells throughout most of the leaf and groups of isodiametric cells in its basal angles. A midrib is present in the leaf of *Funaria*, and the chloroplasts in the leaf cells are large and prominent. No midrib exists in *Hypnum cupressiforme* and the chaff-like leaves are noticeably poor in chloroplasts. Although *Hypnum cupressiforme* is the most notoriously polymorphic British moss, and one of the commonest, it never departs from this description in any essential feature. The differences concern size and habit in the main, though some observers (Guillamot[91], Doignon[62]) have claimed small but constant differences in cell measurements and other fine details between the many so-called varieties of this species.

The above contrast hints at the breadth of gametophyte expression in the Bryidae, but it does not explore it. A dozen examples could be found, differing as widely again in every particular of leaf structure and each of distinctive habit; and many would be found to typify a whole family or sometimes an order of the sub-class Bryidae. Confining himself to British mosses, the interested student would do well to look up descriptions, figures and, better still, specimens of the following illustrative examples: *Fissidens*, *Dicranum*, *Tortula*, *Grimmia*, *Bryum*, *Mnium*, *Bartramia*, *Ulota*, *Fontinalis*, *Neckera*, *Thuidium*, *Rhytidiadelphus*. Among so many small but clear-cut differences of habit, leaf shape and 'pattern' of leaf cell structure it is often difficult to find any that are fundamental. Hence the Bryidae compose a single large, unwieldy sub-class of the class Musci.

Buxbaumia, always a notable genus, and now made more famous as the emblem and title of the Dutch bryological journal, has a very remarkable gametophyte. Perhaps the clearest description and figures of it are those given by Goebel[85], who described *Buxbaumia* male plants as 'about the simplest moss plants we know'. They could hardly be simpler, for they consist only of protonema which bears at the tips of some of its branches a curious hood-like 'leaf' protecting the antheridium. This 'leaf' is bizarre in form and quite minute. It is, however, chlorophyllous. In the slightly more elaborate female plant the protonema alone is green. Unfortunately both British species of *Buxbaumia* are very rare, for it is a genus of the greatest interest, not merely in the present context, but also for its sporophyte and mode of life. Growing always on substrata rich in organic matter, it seems to be in part saprophytic. Although Goebel is often quoted as having believed in widespread reduction among bryophytes, one notices that in the special case of *Buxbaumia* he concluded that it had '*stood still*' in a stage which other Musci had passed. In a word, it is an archaic form. We shall see later on how far a study of its sporophyte bears out this view.

Polytrichum presents a highly organized gametophyte. The genus is large (over 100 species) and of nearly world-wide distribution. Richards and Wallace[197] recognize eleven species as British, of which the largest, *P. commune*, may be taken as an example. The erect gametophores attain a height of 25–30 cm in this species but, as in all typical members of the genus, they spring from a horizontal underground so-called rhizome. This organ bears abundant rhizoids which tend to be massed together and spirally twisted; they have been shown to be important in both external and internal conduction. The anatomy of the stem is complex. The role of a central strand in conduction is controversial (cf. Bowen[21], Mägdefrau[145]) but whatever importance it may have it seems to be supplemented by an external pathway furnished by the widely sheathing leaf bases (cf. Chapter 9). These clasp the stem so closely as to provide a capillary channel (Fig. 18D). They can also make the stem appear glossy when dry—a useful 'field character' for *Polytrichum commune*.

Each leaf consists of the almost colourless sheathing base and a lanceolate 'limb', which in all species of *Polytrichum* appears relatively firm, opaque and dark green. A transverse section shows it to consist of a very wide nerve, flanked by narrow wings of tissue that are one cell thick. The wide nerve is many cells thick and includes both thick-walled and thin-walled elements (Fig. 18E). The firm, opaque character of the leaf arises from close-set rows of lamellae borne on the adaxial surface. Each lamella appears in section as a chain of green cells crowned by a colourless cell. This terminal cell provides an important taxonomic character; it is bifid in *P. commune*. Clearly these lamellae, which in the intact leaf are like green walls running the length of the limb, and separated by extremely narrow spaces, are an important photosynthetic tissue. There are commonly thirty to fifty to a leaf, and they find their closest parallel in the photosynthetic tissue on the upper surface of the thallus in the liverwort *Riccia*. This short summary is enough to indicate in *Polytrichum* a shoot structure that is distinctive in many ways. We must turn to the close allies of *Buxbaumia* and of *Polytrichum* for links between them and more normal moss shoot structure.

Diphyscium foliosum is widespread on turfy banks in north and west Britain, so that material is not difficult to obtain. It possesses the disproportionately large sporophyte and diminutive gametophyte of *Buxbaumia*, and like that genus is dioecious. The male plants, however, are much larger than those of *Buxbaumia* and the female gametophore is a well-developed green leafy shoot. The strap-shaped leaves, much curled when dry, resemble those of some species of *Tortella* and *Trichostomum* among the Bryidae. The laciniate perichaetial bracts are peculiar and the sporophyte proclaims its affinities with that of *Buxbaumia*. Thus, *Diphyscium* provides some link between *Buxbaumia* and more ordinary, unspecialized Bryidae.

The close relatives of *Polytrichum* also provide a link between it and less specialized mosses, so far as gametophytes are concerned. Thus, in species of *Atrichum* the leaves appear filmy in character, with many resemblances to those of *Mnium* species. The nerve is narrow and the lamellae few in number. Again, examination of the sporophyte will leave us in no doubt as to their affinities.

Although gametophyte characters, especially those of the leaf, are so widely used in moss taxonomy we must conclude that for displaying underlying affinities between two plants real resemblances between the two sporophytes are normally essential. The genus *Aloina* (Pottiales), for example, shows a system of lamellae on the adaxial surface of the leaf somewhat like that of *Polytrichum*, but the merest glance at the sporophyte shows that the two genera are quite unrelated. A brief review of these six examples (from five sub-classes of Musci) certainly does not suggest that each sub-class has its own characteristic gametophyte structure. In any case, the genera of Bryidae far outnumber those of all the other four sub-classes together; and it is to the diversity of leafy shoots found among these that attention must now be turned.

Exceedingly small moss gametophytes are not uncommon, the tiny shoots consisting of little more than a few leaves surrounding the groups of sex organs. An extreme case in the British flora is *Ephemerum*, with *E. serratum* its commonest species (Fig. 12H). Here the protonema is long-persistent and the leafy shoots are almost microscopic. Still more extreme is *Ephemeropsis*, with two species, one known from Java, the other from New Zealand and Tasmania. In this genus all leaves are directly associated with sex organs and are only about 0·2 mm long. The plants grow on the surfaces of leaves or twigs and, as Sainsbury[202] points out, without sporophytes the presence of the moss is scarcely detectable, so close is its superficial resemblance to a filamentous green alga. Such examples as this make the gametophyte of *Buxbaumia* appear less isolated. Nor must we forget the surprisingly small (dwarf) male plants that are found in some species of *Dicranum* and certain other genera.

The two most marked modifications of leaf arrangement known are (1) the strictly two-ranked and (2) the strictly three-ranked arrangement, in which the ventral rank is composed of small leaves. A tendency for leafy shoots to become flattened in one plane is not uncommon, being seen in *Plagiothecium*, *Isopterygium* (Fig. 11c), *Neckera*, *Homalia* and some others; but in none of these are the leaves strictly in two ranks, and the usual three-sided apical cell is present. In the enormous genus *Fissidens* (Fig. 11B), by contrast, there are two ranks only and an apical cell with two cutting faces functions for most of the life of the plant. *Fissidens* is odd in another respect, namely in having leaves that are boat-shaped, with an additional wing of tissue. In typical members of the genus this 'wing' is so extensive as to alter completely the appearance of the leaf; and the midrib runs out into it. A link with more normal leaf structure is seen in the related genus *Sorapilla*, where only a small dorsal wing is formed. Strictly two-ranked leaves occur in a few other instances, e.g. in *Distichium* which is thus easily distinguished from other Ditrichaceae, and in scattered examples among non-British genera.

Apart from *Fontinalis* (already mentioned), a symmetrically three-ranked leaf arrangement is found in *Tristichium*, *Triquetrella* and other genera of widely scattered affinities. More remarkable is the situation where the ventral rank of leaves has become reduced in size and the term 'amphigastria' has been borrowed from liverworts to describe them. This is seen well in the family Hypopterygiaceae, with few genera and under 100 species altogether. *Catharomnion* is monotypic and *C. ciliatum*, from New Zealand and Tasmania, is also remarkable for its long-ciliate leaf margins. *Hypopterygium* is by far the largest genus and is widely distributed in the tropics and sub-tropics, extending south to New Zealand and Tasmania. A species of *Hypopterygium* has been established for many years in a rocky, grotto-type conservatory at Reading. Goebel[85] referred to the anisophylly in this genus and indicated its probable derivation from a radially symmetrical shoot structure. In the strange case of *Helicophyllum torquatum*, figured by Brotherus[25], there are actually two ranks of minute amphigastria, one on each side of the mid-ventral line; and the large oblong lateral leaves have their tips curiously inrolled.

Turning to leaf form (already touched upon in *Fissidens*), we find great variety within the British flora, but for some of the most bizarre examples we have to turn to the mosses of other lands. It would be pointless to attempt a catalogue of the diverse leaf forms met with. A study of the illustrations in any good flora will indicate something of the range—from narrowly linear to broadly ovate or sub-orbicular; from leaves that are straight and almost parallel-sided to leaves that (as in some species of *Drepanocladus*) taper to very fine points and are curved almost into a semicircle (cf. Fig. 11F). Leaf shape, character of margin and other morphological features, not to mention finer structure, afford a range of taxonomic characters of great importance. Parallel development must be widespread, however, and phyletic conclusions would seldom rest secure on leaf morphology alone.

Presence or absence of a midrib is usually constant in a particular genus, or even throughout a family. A midrib tends to be present and is often highly organized in most orders of 'acrocarpous' mosses—for example in Dicranales, Pottiales, Eubryales and others. It is much less well developed and is often lacking altogether in many Isobryales, Hookeriales and Hypnobryales. An excurrent, hyaline

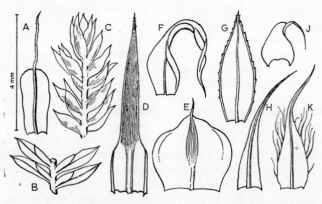

Fig. 11 Gametophyte of mosses A, D, F, G, H and J to show a range of leaf form. B and C. To compare strictly two-ranked leaves with 'flattened' type of leafy shoot. E and K. Special types of leaf. A. *Tortula intermedia*. B. *Fissidens bryoides*. C. *Isopterygium elegans*. D. *Polytrichum juniperinum*. E. Perigonial leaf of the same. F. *Drepanocladus revolvens*. G. *Mnium hornum*. H. *Dicranella heteromalla*. J. *Ctenidium molluscum*. K. *Thuidium tamariscinum*, perichaetial leaf. (All to same magnification)

'hair-point'—composed of dead, air-filled cells—is not uncommon. Among British mosses it is widespread in the genera *Tortula* (Fig. 11A), *Grimmia* and *Rhacomitrium*, occurring sporadically elsewhere. W. Watson[249] has drawn attention to this (together with some other characters of moss leaves) as a type of xerophytic adaptation (cf. Chapter 9).

The frail leaves of mosses are often strengthened by a border of specialized cells, narrow and thick-walled in contrast with those of the rest of the leaf. *Mnium punctatum* and other species of the same genus (Fig. 11G) are good British examples. The whole 'pattern' of leaf cell structure is often highly characteristic of a particular group; witness the prevalence of papillose upper leaf cells in Pottiales; the hexagonal-rhomboid leaf cells in *Bryum* and related genera; the exceedingly long, narrow leaf cells in *Drepanocladus*, and so on. Indeed, the whole arrangement of different kinds of cells in the moss leaf constitutes a rich source of taxonomic characters; and leaf cell structure has always to be examined when one is determining moss species.

To conclude these remarks on leaf form, one may refer to *Rhizofabronia sphaerocarpa*, from West Africa, which is figured by Brotherus[25] and must surely show one of the most extraordinary kinds of leaf to be found among mosses. The minute leaves could in a sense be described as pinnate, but the 'lateral members' are no more than extensively projecting individual cells.

It remains to consider the rhizoid system and then to say a few words concerning the special leaves borne on reproductive shoots. Many small, erect-growing mosses possess a well-developed rhizoid system which is in close contact with the substratum. Thus, when specimens of some of these small 'acrocarps' are collected for study it will be found that each little plant is provided with freely branched rhizoids which penetrate the soil to a depth at least equal to, and often exceeding, the height of the leafy shoot. This may be seen very well in some of the low-growing colonists of chalky soil, such as *Dicranella varia*, *Pottia davalliana*, various species of *Barbula* and others. Analogy with a root system is obvious, but in some ways a closer parallel is with root hairs. For the finer branches of the rhizoid system are very slender and quite colourless, with extremely delicate cell walls; also, they may become mis-shapen at their tips where in close contact with soil particles. The coarser strands are apparently both anchoring and conducting, and Goebel[85] explained their commonly oblique cross walls as an adaptation to facilitate faster conduction. These coarser strands are often brown, and sometimes their cell walls are papillose. Often there are perhaps half a dozen of these directed more or less vertically downwards and from them the obliquely placed, finer laterals arise which in turn bear the very delicate tertiary branches referred to above. A specimen of

Fissidens taxifolius, which grew on soil in an Oxfordshire beechwood, proved revealing when carefully soaked out. The leafy shoots attained a height of 1 cm, the matted rhizoid system a depth of fully 3 cm.

Other mosses are remarkably deficient in rhizoids. This is true especially of many freely branched Hypnobryales where close contact with the substratum seems to be lost at an early age and the straggling older shoot systems are not anchored at all. Reference has already been made to the absence of rhizoids from mature *Sphagnum*. Elsewhere a dense covering of rhizoids clothes the stem for much of its length. This has been variously termed 'tomentum' and 'radicles' by systematic bryologists. Such rhizoids clothe the stems of *Polytrichum alpestre* in a dense whitish felt. They are well developed in some forms of *Dicranum scoparium*; and may be seen in many other mosses. The dense and almost continuous rhizoid covering of the stem in *Aulacomnium palustre* has often been cited as a good specific character. However, as mentioned by Sayre (in Grout's *Moss flora of North America*, vol. II) and emphasized by Wallace[197], a rather similar, though less dense, rhizoidal covering is also found on the stems of the arctic-alpine *Aulacomnium turgidum*.

In all these cases the 'tomentum' is a dense tangle of rhizoidal branches of varying calibre. The most slender may be only 3 μ in width and are sometimes swollen at their tips. Unlike subaerial protonema filaments they are not green. Rhizoid systems in which laterals come to lie along the same axis as main strands were detected in some species of *Polytrichum* more than a century ago. They have been likened to 'twisted string', and Goebel has commented on their manner of functioning like a wick in conduction. Wigglesworth[260], much more recently, has demonstrated that they can also be important in vegetative reproduction (cf. Chapter 7). There can be little doubt that any moss stem bearing a dense rhizoidal covering is well equipped for external capillary conduction of water. It is also possible to visualize the significance of such rhizoids for water retention and absorption, for the main strands are direct outgrowths of superficial cells of the stem. Performing a like function, but much less widely distributed among mosses, are the paraphyllia. These clothe the main stems of *Hylocomium splendens*, *Thuidium tamariscinum* and some others. They are like minute, richly branched leaves of variable and irregular shape.

In many instances the leaves surrounding groups of reproductive organs are little different from vegetative leaves. In *Bryum*, *Funaria* and other genera the leaf size increases upwards on the stem, the largest leaves forming a group around the insertion of the sex organs. Those surrounding archegonial groups are known as perichaetial leaves; those investing antheridial clusters as perigonial leaves. In a single species the two may be widely different in form. Thus, in *Polytrichum* species the perigonial leaves are much the more strongly modified, and each consists of a very broad sheathing base and a short bristle point (Fig. 11E). In *P. juniperinum* they are red-brown or olive; in *P. piliferum* dull red. One sees the same marked change of form in the leaves that compose the bud-like 'male inflorescences' of autoecious species of *Bryum* and *Pohlia*; or again in *Philonotis* where the broadly expanded perigonial leaves give the antheridial receptacles a flower-like appearance and also provide a useful taxonomic character. The leaves that protect the antheridia in some species of *Fissidens* lack the characteristic 'wing' of that genus.

Perichaetial leaves, too, can be strikingly modified. Those investing the archegonia in many Hypnobryales are often nearly colourless, concave and long-acuminate; they must be efficient protective structures. They serve also to hold water—so essential to fertilization in bryophytes—and this has been taken to be the explanation of the laciniate tips of the perichaetial leaves in *Diphyscium*, and the even more strikingly 'ciliate' perichaetial leaves of some species of *Thuidium* (Fig. 11K). One need not emphasize that the chief work of the moss gametophyte is to bear sex organs; and it is not surprising therefore that many adaptations of leaf form have been evolved for their efficient protection and water supply. The form, arrangement and association with paraphyses of the sex organs themselves will be considered in Chapter 8.

In conclusion one must admit that, for all their diversity, the gametophytes of mosses do not compare in range of form with those of liverworts. Admittedly, they present many notably different kinds of habit, some of them very arresting. In this country we know the 'miniature trees' of *Climacium*, the 'moss balls' of *Leucobryum* and the festooning mats of *Neckera crispa*, to mention only three. Others are better seen elsewhere, and Martin[150] in his notes on the moss flora of New Zealand has referred graphically to forests where mosses are of real importance. He alludes to the 'yellowish-grey streamers of *Weymouthia*', and the 'golden tresses of pendent *Papillaria*'. Then again, there are the very large and the excessively minute among mosses; but if one measures diversity by the range of form exhibited by fundamental component structures the conclusion is inescapable. For leafy liverworts offer entire, two-, three- and four-lobed leaves; elaborately ciliate leaves such as those of *Trichocolea* and *Ptilidium*; complicate-bilobed leaves with elaborate sac formation as in *Frullania*; and mosses show none of these developments. True, in many mosses there is a complexity of internal organization in the leaf (and in the stem) unmatched by any liverwort, but the underlying diversity is lacking. Parihar[173] has estimated that there are some 14,000 known species of Bryidae, as against 7,000 leafy liverworts. Yet a study of their gametophyte structure reveals them as a relatively circumscribed group. Therein lies one of the difficulties of the taxonomist. For an accurate account of the leaf forms the basis of good descriptions of species; and the moss leaf presents, after all, only innumerable minor variations on a common plan.

6

The sporophyte of mosses

THE sporophytes of Musci (mosses) show the same fundamental parts as those of Hepaticae, but there is a difference of emphasis. The foot is less often bulbous or anchor-shaped, more usually dagger-like in form. The seta is a stronger and much longer-lived structure than in liverworts. Lengthening early, it contrasts with the seta of liverworts which lengthens only after the spores are mature, sometimes (e.g. *Pellia*) actually after they have germinated in the capsule. Also, there is greater tissue differentiation within the seta of a moss. Though slender, it is tough, and in some cases (e.g. *Pohlia nutans*) may persist long after the capsule has matured and perished. The most notable divergence, however, occurs in the capsule itself, which in a typical moss is an important organ of photosynthesis for much of its life. It has been calculated that the photosynthetic capacity of the capsule of *Funaria hygrometrica* is equivalent to that of fourteen leaves (of the gametophyte). Stomata are normally present. Although sporogenous tissue (in all but *Sphagnum*) is derived from internal layers (endothecium), there is a well-defined columella. Hence the capsule of a typical moss is nearer to that of *Anthoceros* than to any other liverwort, although there are very important differences, such as the absence of a basal meristem and the entirely different mode of dehiscence. Moreover, elaters are unknown in the Musci. Thus, the moss sporophyte, in all normal examples, is only a partial parasite on the gametophyte; and it is more highly organized internally than any liverwort with the possible exception of *Anthoceros*.

Even so, it is difficult to make generalizations that hold good for all mosses; and we may mention now some of the important exceptions, where the sporophyte structure differs from that outlined

77

above. As might be expected, two of the most notable are *Sphagnum* and *Andreaea*, each the genus which typifies a whole order of mosses, and each rather far removed from all others. On wet moors and bogs during June one may find some species of *Sphagnum* rather commonly fruiting, and the pale greenish, nearly globose capsules can be detected amongst the leaves of the terminal cluster of shoots. By mid-July, or sometimes rather earlier, each capsule will be raised on a short stalk, or pseudopodium, of gametophyte origin, for there is no true seta here. The capsule itself will have become dark brown, and as it dries in the sunshine it shrinks until the air that it contains is held under considerable pressure. With mounting pressure of air within there comes a moment when the small, convex lid is blown off and the spores escape in a cloud. The air, hitherto confined, is suddenly released, and Ingold[111] refers to it as the 'air gun' mechanism of spore discharge. Lack of seta and mode of dehiscence are but two of the peculiarities in the sporophyte of *Sphagnum*. Two others are the dome-shaped spore sac and the development of sporogenous tissue from a superficial layer—the amphithecium. This last is a character in common with *Anthoceros* and a point of difference from all other mosses.

Andreaea agrees with ordinary mosses in having internal (endothecial) origin of spore-producing tissue; but on all other counts it is just as unusual as *Sphagnum*. Thus, the spore sac extends like a dome over the central columella instead of surrounding it in the form of a cylindrical sheath, as in other mosses; and a gametophyte pseudopodium again functions in place of a true seta. The most striking peculiarity of the sporophyte of *Andreaea*, however, lies in the capsule itself. This is minute and ovoid, tapering a little at base and apex. Longitudinally it is marked by four lines of weaker cells and as the capsule ripens its wall splits along these four lines, whilst remaining intact above and below. The four valves that result (Fig. 13E) are very sensitive to changes in moisture. If one examines the mountain rock faces, where *Andreaea rupestris* can often be found with sporophytes, on a dry, sunny day, the valves can be seen gaping widely apart; but as soon as they are thoroughly wetted they close up and the capsule resumes the ovoid form it had before dehiscence. Measuring only *c.* 0·5 mm in length, the capsule of *Andreaea* must be among the smallest known, and its chlorophyll content appears meagre. There can be no doubt that the placing of *Sphagnum* and *Andreaea* respectively in two quite separate orders of the class Musci is amply borne out by this rapid review of the salient features of the sporophyte of each.

By contrast, *Funaria hygrometrica* can be taken as typifying a host of ordinary genera of the Bryidae (Eubrya of Smith). For in this large group the sporophytes of different genera, or even families, differ in only minor points. All agree in that sporogenous tissue is formed from the innermost layers of the early embryo; in all the spore sac is cylindrical, not dome-shaped; and all show the expected differentiation into foot, seta and capsule. There is no need to repeat in detail here the well-known sequence of events in *Funaria*, for it is to be found in almost every general textbook, and further details of its sporophyte are given in the New Biology series of 'Famous Plants'[245].

To trace the stages from tiny ellipsoidal embryo encased in archegonial venter, through the spindle-shaped middle period when the calyptra has swollen in advance of the capsule, to the functional stage of the pear-shaped green capsule, makes a fascinating study. It can be carried on through the stages of waning photosynthetic activity, as the capsule turns first yellow, then orange and finally dark brown, and the lid is forcibly removed by the swelling annular cells and the spores are shed. This last process must often be very gradual, controlled as it is by the hygroscopic movements of the outer ring of peristome teeth. Two unusual features here are that both sets of sixteen teeth are on the same radii and that the outer teeth are united terminally in a little disc of tissue. A remarkable fact about *Funaria hygrometrica*, and one which is very useful to the teaching botanist, is its capacity to show a wide assortment of different sporophyte stages within a single colony. Greene and Greene[87] have recently drawn up a scheme for comparing different mosses with respect to the 'time-table' of events in their life cycles. It would be interesting to see what kind of analysis emerged for *Funaria*, for it surely shows exceptional latitude. We must pass on now, however, to give a comparative account of the sporophytes of the Bryidae. It is convenient to distinguish between (1) early stages,

(2) the functional green stage (of capsule) and (3) the stage of dehiscence and spore discharge.

(1) *Early stages.* According to Campbell[35] the majority of Bryidae which were examined embryologically showed close agreement in the early stages of the sporophyte. Polarity is acquired at the outset and the young sporophyte (whatever its ultimate form) elongates rapidly through the activity of an apical cell. Normally a second apical cell functions at the lower extremity of the sporophyte, and the whole structure changes from ovoid to ellipsoid, and finally to a narrowly cylindrical form, tapering at each extremity. The foot penetrates deeply into gametophyte tissue and, as in *Funaria*, the external differentiation distally into seta and capsule is delayed (Fig. 12L). Transverse sections through the young embryo show that periclinal divisions early mark off the central endothecium from the peripheral amphithecium; and thereafter the forerunners of spore mother cells (archesporium) become recognizable within the endothecium, but not until the whole structure is some twenty cells in thickness, and both central columella and external wall are well differentiated. It would appear from Campbell's figures that this degree of differentiation is not reached until the capsule starts to swell. The seta of course begins to lengthen fairly early in mosses, and in species like *Ceratodon purpureus* and *Pohlia nutans*, which over-winter with young sporophytes, a colour contrast can be observed before the capsule has begun to swell. At this time the reddish-purple seta contrasts with the pale green terminal capsular region. Subsequent changes in the capsule are more marked in *Pohlia* than in *Ceratodon* for in the former it is finally pyriform and pendulous, whereas the capsule of *Ceratodon* (or that of *Tortula*) remains cylindrical and erect. Where the ultimate shape of the capsule is sub-spherical, as in *Bartramia*, more rapid and extensive changes must take place at a certain critical stage of development.

Rather little seems to be known regarding the mechanisms controlling these important changes whereby the sporophyte goes forward from a comparatively undifferentiated early stage to one in which we can see foot, seta and capsule all well defined and displaying a characteristic structure. Clearly, the speed of events must vary greatly from one species to another. In early winter ephemerals such as *Phascum cuspidatum* all the steps from fertilization to fully swollen green capsule must be accomplished in a few weeks; in many instances where fertilization is a summer event, and capsules ripen in the following May or June, a much longer period obtains (e.g. species of *Dicranella, Tortula, Bryum, Mnium*, etc.); whilst fertilization and maturation of capsules are separated by up to thirteen months in *Polytrichum*. Again, it must be borne in mind that many mosses lack a prolonged green stage, and pass quickly from capsule swelling to that of dehiscence and spore discharge. In this connection more biological studies of selected species are required. A really full study of events in a chosen species would fill many gaps in our knowledge.

(2) *The functional, 'green capsule' stage.* 'Functional' here refers to a stage of maximum photosynthetic activity and that of course embraces but one aspect of the function of a moss sporophyte. Biologically it is of great importance in establishing some degree of independence for the sporophyte as regards sources of organic matter; and in the evolutionary context it is important because it shows us the moss sporogonium nearer to an independent green land plant than it is at any other time; and this may indicate its progress towards the Pteridophyta, or its derivation from that group (cf. Christensen[47]) according to the trend of one's evolutionary thinking. Campbell[35] pointed out that this green sporophyte in mosses had a lower proportion of its tissues given over to spore production than had any other bryophyte. This to him indicated a derived condition, for his thought was in line with that of Bower[23], who in 1908 had pointed to an 'origin of a land flora' by the sterilization of ever-increasing amounts of potentially sporogenous tissue. Nowhere among bryophytes was so much tissue thus 'sterilized' as in the green capsule (together with the seta and foot) of mosses. When one turns from these views to those of Christensen[47] and others one sees that 'the wheel has turned full circle'; for the greener, the more highly organized and more nearly independent the sporophyte is, the more primitive it is thought to be. There is no common ground between the two points of view.

In range of capsule form at the green stage one finds considerable diversity; sufficient indeed to provide the taxonomist with some useful systematic characters. Important differences between different members of the Bryidae based on internal characters of the green sporophyte do not appear to have been recognized, although it is possible that they may exist. I have examined the foot, in transverse and longitudinal sections, in several species and it appears always to be well differentiated into outer, intermediate and central tissues. These are, respectively, composed of highly protoplasmic haustorial cells, ordinary parenchymatous cells, and narrow elongated cells which would seem to be conducting in function. In each case (*Mnium, Bryum, Atrichum*) the foot is more or less parallel-sided, tapering rather than bulbous at its tip, and deeply penetrating. This important structure is of course concealed in life (and in herbarium specimens), and little has been written about it from the comparative standpoint. Lorch[138] indicates that only occasionally is the haustorial character of the peripheral layer of cells really well marked. One has to turn to seta and capsule for well defined family or generic distinctions.

The seta varies from a minute structure in cleistocarpous genera such as *Ephemerum* and *Phascum* to a notably elongated organ specialized for support and conduction. In general, a seta over 5 cm long is exceptional. Even the massive seta of the tall *Polytrichum commune* seldom exceeds 5 cm by much; but I have measured a seta over 7 cm long in *Pohlia nutans*, and one exceeding 10 cm in *Drepanocladus fluitans*. In this last instance great length of seta is at times necessary for raising the capsule clear of the water in the deep bog pools that this species inhabits. The seta of *Polytrichum commune* is almost 0·5 mm in diameter; that of *Pohlia nutans*, in common with most other mosses, is only about 0·2 mm in diameter.

This slender organ has been much used taxonomically because it can often give minor but clean-cut and constant differences between related genera or species, especially differences of colour or papillosity. Use is made of the former character in *Dicranella*, of the latter in *Brachythecium* and *Eurhynchium*, in separating pairs of closely related species. The papillae on the seta of *Brachythecium rutabulum* are large enough to be easily visible with a hand lens. The colour of the seta, characteristically red in *Dicranella varia*, and yellow in *D. heteromalla*, cannot always be relied upon. I have seen the seta of *Funaria hygrometrica* red, although it is normally greenish yellow, and when old or flooded setae (like capsules) may become discoloured and blackish.

Most of the principal orders of mosses are marked by their own characteristic form of capsule. It is narrowly cylindrical and erect in such a genus as *Ditrichum* in the Dicranales, and in *Tortula* in the Pottiales. It is pyriform and pendulous in many species of *Bryum*

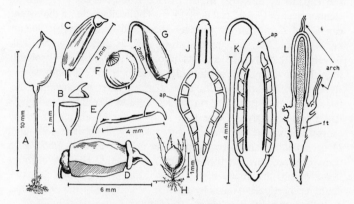

Fig. 12 Some types of moss capsule. A. *Buxbaumia aphylla*. B. *Pottia truncata*. C. *Ceratodon purpureus*. D. *Polytrichum commune*. E. *Eurhynchium striatum*. F. *Bartramia pomiformis*. G. *Bryum pendulum*. H. *Ephemerum serratum*. J. *Splachnum ampullaceum* (L. S.). K. *Mnium hornum* (L. S.). L. Young sporophyte of a moss, semidiagrammatic. ap. apophysis; arch. archegonial neck; ft. foot. Sporogenous tissue is shown black in J and K. In A the seta is included; also the minute gametophyte.

and *Pohlia*, subglobose in *Bartramia* and *Philonotis*, and a short, curved structure in many genera of the Hypnobryales (cf. Fig. 12). Both shape an d inclination (erect, inclined, horizontal or pendulous) are important characters taxonomically, but no systematic bryologist is satisfied with the green stage, since it lacks the highly significant details of peristome and spores. The real interest of the green stage is biological, and it is pertinent to enquire to what extent the various features seen in the green capsule of *Funaria* are present also in other mosses. A few examples may be cited.

One will usually find the principal regions represented, apophysis and theca (spore-producing region), and in the latter, 'water jacket' layers of wall, chlorophyllous tissue, air spaces, spore sac and columella. The main differences lie in the proportions of these (Fig. 12). Thus, in *Bryum capillare* the sporogenous tissue occupies a rather narrow zone in the transverse section, because the wall of the capsule is massive, the air space extensive (and crossed by slender strands termed trabeculae), the columella wide. In the rotund capsule of *Bartramia* the wide air space and slender trabeculae are again notable. Also, in stout capsules such as these the green tissue is very well developed and its photosynthetic capacity probably high. Narrowly cylindrical capsules, such as those of *Amblystegium serpens* and *Tortula muralis*, have a much narrower air space between wall and spore sac, trabeculae are less developed and green tissue less extensive. There is a many-layered wall and a broad central columella, but the cells composing both these regions tend to be smaller than the corresponding cells in *Bryum capillare*. In transverse sections cut in February I found that the sporogenous tissue occupied a much higher proportion of the whole, but this could be partly explained by the fact that the capsule of *Tortula muralis* was slightly further developed than that of *Bryum capillare*. It is interesting to notice that the epidermal cells of the green capsule are comparatively thin-walled in *Amblystegium serpens*, but have greatly thickened and cutinized walls in *Tortula muralis*. There would seem to be a correlation with habitat here, for the latter species is found in notably drier and more exposed situations. I found that the columella cells of *Tortula muralis* held much starch at this stage, those of *Bryum capillare* little or none. It is clear that there are many points here which would repay fuller investigation.

Two features of the green capsule which call for further discussion are the extent of the apophysis and the number and distribution of stomata. In many mosses the spore-bearing region passes over into the seta with little obvious development of neck (apophysis), although there will doubtless be more internal differentiation than is betrayed by the external form. Species of *Bryum* and *Pohlia* sometimes surpass *Funaria hygrometrica* in the development of a well defined neck region, but it is in the Splachnaceae that we find the most extensive apophysis of all. Members of this family are of interest for several reasons, not least because they mostly live on organic substrata, and this specialized habitat is linked with the big development of apophysis. The two commonest British species are *Splachnum ampullaceum*, which lives exclusively on dung, and *Tetraplodon mnioides* which grows mainly on decaying bones. The former has very much the larger apophysis, which is indeed many times the size of the theca (Fig. 12J). In certain non-British species, e.g. *Splachnum luteum, S. rubrum*, it is larger still and forms a yellow or red parasol-like growth unmatched elsewhere in mosses (for plate see Wettstein, R.[253], p. 297). It appears that this specialized apophysis is not only conspicuous in size and colour; it is also attractive to dung flies through a secretion which it yields; thus these flies assist in the dissemination of the spores.

Paton and Pearce[178] have undertaken a broad survey of stomatal occurrence, structure and function in British mosses, and they point out that where the apophysis is large (as in *Splachnum*) the stomata tend also to be numerous. It is difficult, however, to explain the widely different numbers of stomata found in different species where the capsules are of normal size and proportions. Thus, over 200 stomata per capsule were found in some species of *Philonotis*, but much lower numbers than this are usual. In some cleistocarpous mosses e.g. *Pleuridium* spp., only three or four stomata were found per capsule. Rather strangely, capsules that lacked stomata were found in widely divergent groups of mosses. Some were aquatics, like *Fontinalis antipyretica*, but others were terrestrial, for example all species of *Atrichum* and some of *Polytrichum*. Clearly it is possible for some moss capsules to have a satisfactory functional life in the absence of the openings to the exterior which stomata provide. Furthermore, the stomata often become permanently closed with the advancing age of the capsule, and Paton and Pearce remark that even when the capsule is young and green these stomata lack sensitivity to such influences as changes in light intensity or carbon dioxide concentration. During this period they provide access to the internal atmosphere of the capsule and, we are told, 'close only when the water content of the capsule itself is greatly reduced, owing to extreme drought'. In some species the stomata are deeply sunk beneath the surface of the epidermis, but the incidence of this shows no clear correlation with dry habitats. Indeed in the genus *Orthotrichum* one finds 'superficial' and 'immersed' stomata in related species of similar ecological amplitude. Such a clear-cut difference has been useful to the taxonomist making keys to the species of this genus.

(3) *The stage of dehiscence and spore discharge.* With the gradual ripening of the capsule we have access to its most valuable taxonomic character, the peristome. This surrounds the mouth of the capsule after the lid has been shed. The teeth composing the single peristome of some mosses (Aplolepideae) and the outer peristome of others (Diplolepideae) are composed of a kind of two-ply material furnished by the cell walls of adjacent cells. Ordinarily sixteen teeth spring from the diaphragm at the mouth of the capsule, their bases forming a rather close-fitting circle, their apices tapering to quite fine points. There is much variety of detail. One may cite the twisted cone of *Tortula subulata*, the sixteen cleft teeth of *Dicranella heteromalla* (Fig. 13A), the eight pairs of reflexed teeth in *Orthotrichum*, to mention only a few. Almost always, however, the main ring of teeth (the outer peristome when this is double) consists of relatively firm, golden brown, barred structures, the bars revealing the limits of the cells whose walls have persisted to form the tooth; and owing to their two-ply structure and the uneven deposition of their thickening these principal teeth are sensitive to changes in humidity. When a complete inner peristome is present it consists essentially of a pale tubular membrane which supports a surprisingly elaborate superstructure. For arising from this basal membrane, and alternating with the sixteen outer teeth, are sixteen cleft or fenestrate inner teeth, whilst on the same radii as the outer teeth are groups of thread-like 'cilia' (Fig. 13H). These cilia commonly occur three or four together, and when perfectly developed have short transverse appendages.

In some genera, for instance *Bryum, Pohlia,* one finds certain species that have a complete double peristome, with appendiculate cilia, but in the same genus there are others in which it is to varying degrees imperfect. In these the cilia may be represented by mere stumps and appear to be vestigial. Indeed, there is evidence that here and there, in widely different circles of affinity, the peristome has undergone reduction; and this has sometimes been so drastic that the structure has been lost altogether. Formerly bryologists placed all such mosses together in a separate group, but nowadays it is universally recognized that a moss which has lost its peristome may be closely related to other species in which this structure has been retained. Thus, to mention two examples, *Pottia lanceolata* is peristomate, *P. truncata* (Fig. 12B) is gymnostomous; in *Funaria hygrometrica* the peristome is well developed (and double); in *F. fascicularis* it is rudimentary or lost.

In the classification of mosses greater reliance has probably been placed on the peristome than on any other character, so that it has formed the basis of the main sub-divisions of Bryidae. The peristome, for example, is characteristic, and quite different, in each of the orders, Dicranales, Pottiales and Eubryales. Yet, like all taxonomic characters and all indications of affinity, it must not be used inflexibly. Thus in the genus *Encalypta* there is no reason to doubt that the different species compose a thoroughly natural group. Yet among the British species alone one finds in *Encalypta streptocarpa* a double peristome, in *E. rhabdocarpa* a single peristome and in *E. commutata* no peristome at all.

Some moss capsules have not only lost the peristome but are without a detachable operculum or lid. These are known as cleistocarpous species and the 'closed fruit' opens eventually in an irregular manner to release the spores. The minute *Ephemerum serratum* (Fig. 12H), which may sometimes be found on mud at the margins of ponds, is a good example. It is generally held that even cleistocarpous species may not be distantly related to others that have peristomate capsules.

Turning to the question of spore discharge, one can say that after the lid has been shed the rate at which spores leave the capsule is determined by the peristome. Goebel[85] reviewed the more important arrangements and distinguished between what he called primitive, intermediate and complex types. An example of his primitive condition is provided by certain species of *Barbula* and *Tortula*, in which Goebel held that the long, spirally twisted peristome teeth functioned as a 'hygroscopic lid'. It is true that the peristome of such a species as *Barbula unguiculata* (Fig. 13c) assumes very different appearances in wet and dry conditions, but Goebel's point is that active movements of the teeth themselves play little or no part in effecting the dispersal. An intermediate case is that of *Dicranella heteromalla*, with its single ring of sixteen forked, freely moving teeth (Fig. 13A). Here the spores accumulating under the mouth of

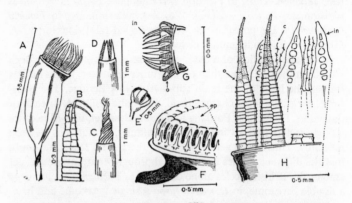

Fig. 13 Structure of moss peristomes. A. *Dicranella heteromalla*. B. Single tooth from same. C. *Barbula unguiculata*. D. *Tetraphis pellucida*. E. *Andreaea rupestris*. F. *Polytrichum commune*. G. *Hypnum cupressiforme*. H. *Bryum capillare*. A, C, D, E and G are all shown as they appear when dry. F. shows small part of capsule with lid removed. In H. part of outer peristome removed. ep. epiphragm; c. cilia; in. inner peristome tooth; o. outer peristome tooth.

the shrinking capsule become caught among the slowly moving peristome teeth, and are shed. Goebel's 'complex' type is illustrated by the double peristome of such genera as *Bryum*, *Mnium* and many others, including a vast range of Hypnobryales. In most of these there is rather more active participation by the teeth in spore dispersal than one can see in the 'bowing' movements of the *Funaria* peristome. *Brachythecium velutinum*, described in detail by Ingold[111], is a good example. Here, in dry conditions, the inner peristome stands up as a pale central cone and the tips of the arched outer peristome teeth are inserted into the gaps between the various inner structures. By such a device spores can be actively flicked out. *Hypnum cupressiforme* (Fig. 13G) is similar. It is usual to find the spores in a ripe capsule massed near the mouth and it seems that the gradual shrinkage of the organ as it ages will always tend to achieve this effect. Once this position of the spore content is attained, it is easy to see how the peristome can function to permit their gradual discharge.

In a recent paper Ingold[112] has thrown some light on these questions, and directed attention to outstanding problems. He points out that in *Mnium hornum* the spores are not sticky and therefore tend to fall naturally towards the mouth of the pendulous capsule. As some are released, others will fall into position. He tested a capsule of *Eurhynchium confertum* by alternately breathing upon it and allowing it to dry, in order to see how effective was discharge by peristome tooth movement alone. The capsule was laid on its side on a glass slide; the procedure was repeated 171 times and a total of 15,647 spores were discharged. Such observations demonstrate the efficiency of the peristome mechanism for securing a gradual liberation of the spores; and, as Ingold points out, an important feature of the whole peristome apparatus is its power of closing the capsule in moist conditions, thereby eliminating spore discharge at such times. Rather baffling, however, is the fact that in dry conditions one has only to agitate the seta violently to induce the liberation of a visible cloud of spores. This at least is so for many mosses, at whatever angle the capsule rests, and with wind and animal movements operative in natural conditions one is led to question whether the gradual discharge that can be demonstrated on a slide in the laboratory does indeed always take place in the field. True, successive agitations of the seta liberate further clouds of spores, but the number of spores in each cloud must amount at least to thousands.

Ingold reports total spore contents of capsules in *Eurhynchium confertum*, as determined by haemacytometer techniques, between 280,000 and 700,000. The capsule in this species is not notably large and these figures seem astonishingly high. My own rough estimates made from time to time on species of *Bryum* and *Pohlia* have led me to total figures much lower than this. Doubtless there is some correlation with size of spore. In many Hypnobryales (to which *Eurhynchium* belongs) the spores are indeed very small, with diameters of 7–10 μ. In the genus *Bryum* there is great diversity, for whereas many species have spores quite as small as the above, those of others attain 20–30 μ, and the spores of *B. warneum* may reach 50 μ in diameter. Records of spore outputs in these different species would be of interest. Ingold considers that the whole subject of spore discharge in mosses is ripe for experimental study. By such means we might learn more of the real significance of that strangely complex but taxonomically useful structure, the moss peristome.

We have seen that it is partly on account of their unusual sporophytes that the genera *Sphagnum* and *Andreaea* are made respectively the basis for separate sub-classes, Sphagnidae and Andreaeidae. Rather surprisingly, there exist certain groups in the Bryidae in which the capsule shows important departures from the kind of structure described in the preceding pages. The most notable examples are *Archidium* and *Tetraphis*. Also, Polytrichidae and Buxbaumiidae display unusual types of sporophyte.

Turning to the first of these, we find in *Archidium* a most unusual moss. The gametophyte is ordinary enough, being much like that of numerous genera in the order Dicranales. The capsule, however, is not merely cleistocarpous; it is without a columella and produces only four to twenty-eight exceedingly large spores (200 μ in diameter). The foot is nearly spherical and there is no seta. Many authors have seen it as an archaic type. Even if reduced, it may well represent a very ancient line of descent to simplicity.

Tetraphis pellucida is interesting for several reasons (cf. Chapter 7), but not least for its capsules. These are perhaps not as commonly produced in Britain as in some parts of its Continental range, but even so they are not rare. In southern England I have found them most plentifully in the spring following a wet late summer. They are well worth close examination. Erect and cylindrical, the capsule as a whole bears a superficial resemblance to those of such genera as *Tortula* and *Barbula*, but a lens reveals that the peristome is composed here of only four large teeth of solid construction (Fig. 13D), more akin to those of *Polytrichum* and its allies. They are, however, held erect in the ripe capsule and there is no trace of an epiphragm.

They would not appear able to effect gradual dispersal of the spores.

We have seen in the last chapter that the Polytrichidae offered some unique features of the gametophyte. This is no less true of the sporophyte. For here, in place of a radial division of peristome into sixteen barred units (with or without the addition of inner structures) one sees thirty-two or sixty-four teeth of an entirely different type. They are peculiarly solid structures, each tooth being composed of fibre-like cells several layers in thickness. Moreover, these teeth are joined at their tips to a pale membrane, the epiphragm, which is stretched like the tympanum of a drum across the capsule mouth after the operculum has been shed. The spores are thus dispersed by a censer mechanism through the minute holes between successive teeth (Fig. 13F). With reason, it has been likened to a poppy capsule. *Polytrichum*, *Atrichum* and *Oligotrichum* all show this structure and the white epiphragm is a conspicuous feature of old capsules in many of the species; especially so perhaps in *Polytrichum aloides*, against the dark background of the shaded recesses where it grows.

Finally, in *Buxbaumia* (Fig. 12A) and the allied *Diphyscium* we find a capsule which immediately arrests attention on account of its large size in relation to the small gametophyte, and its very obvious asymmetry. The peristome is also unusual. In *Diphyscium* the outer peristome is defective or absent and the inner takes the form of a delicate, whitish 'pleated' cone, not closely matched elsewhere. *Buxbaumia* has the same type of inner peristome, but the outer consists, according to the species, of one or several rings of thread-like teeth. Several concentric rings of cells are involved in the formation of this outer peristome and it is evident that the teeth here cannot be homologous with those of ordinary peristomes. Dixon[58] alluded to these plants as representing most probably the survival of an ancient pattern of moss structure, and to supporters of Bower's antithetic theory of bryophyte evolution this would certainly be a reasonable view. Goebel's views on these strange mosses have been cited at an earlier point (cf. p. 67). There is much here to suggest a primitive survival. At all events, it would be difficult to present a convincing argument for the derivation of such a strange peristome from the typical structure found, with minor variants, throughout the great body of the Bryidae. We must not forget that the latter comprise more than 90% of all known mosses. It is surely the aberrant, so few and so unlike the rest, that represent the survival of other, less successful evolutionary lines. This is so in other great taxonomic groups, in flowering plants for example, and again in birds and mammals.

7

Asexual reproduction

ASEXUAL reproduction in bryophytes can be achieved in three ways: by growth and branching, followed by the death and decay of older parts; by the separation of whole organs and the regeneration of new plants from them; and thirdly, by means of specialized units of propagation termed gemmae.

The first method is more widespread than is generally realized. It is claimed, for example, that the plate-like protonema of *Sphagnum* bears initially but one gametophore. If this is so, then the dense tuft or cushion so characteristic of mature plants must have arisen by repeated branching and the subsequent death of older branches. A similar outcome can be seen in liverworts, for example in *Riccia*, where not only the rosette form of the mature gametophyte but also the vegetative spread of the plant may be achieved in this way. It is often impossible, however, to decide how far the mature condition of a moss results from the process just outlined and how far it is caused by numerous buds springing from the original protonema. In any event this is a process calculated more to increase the bulk of the plant than to allow of its spread to entirely new ground. It is scarcely vegetative propagation in the full sense.

The separation of whole organs, on the other hand, can be a most effective means of spreading a plant. The best known examples among mosses are whole shoots or shoot tips, and two common heathland mosses will serve as illustrations. In the first, *Pohlia nutans*, one can often find numbers of the somewhat catkin-like deciduous branches scattered over the surface of the 'short turf' which this plant forms. They appear light against the dark green of the parent moss and the leaves which they bear are small and closely appressed. Even commoner is the sight of the deciduous, light-coloured shoot tips on the deep green patches of *Campylopus piriformis*, a colonist of bare peat and decaying stumps. In this species and the closely related *Campylopus flexuosus* rhizoids are produced freely at the leaf base; these no doubt facilitate regeneration from the deciduous shoot tips.

It is likely that many species which are widely distributed despite infrequent production of sporophytes are able to spread by means of deciduous shoots or shoot fragments in this way; but we have little precise information. Species that spring to mind are *Pleurozium schreberi* and *Pseudoscleropodium purum*. The former is a very common moss on heather moor, the latter the most widespread species generally on chalk grassland. Yet in neither are sporophytes common and in *Pleurozium* they are decidedly rare. Tamm[226] in his detailed study of *Hylocomium splendens* was led to suspect some such means of vegetative spread in that species and was puzzled too by the rarity of young stages in the field. *Myurium hebridarum*, a characteristic and locally plentiful moss in the Outer Hebrides, undoubtedly must spread by deciduous branches, for the sporophyte has never been found in Britain.

Degenkolbe[57], in a comprehensive survey of the organs of vegetative propagation in leafy liverworts, recognized the importance of deciduous branches (Brutäste) and leaves in this connection. He concluded that deciduous branches were an important means of spread for many genera of epiphyllous liverworts in the tropics, all of them members of the family Lejeuneaceae. As examples of deciduous leaves effecting propagation he cited species of *Plagiochila*, *Bazzania* and *Drepanolejeunea*, also two British liverworts, *Mylia cuneifolia* and *Frullania fragilifolia*. Degenkolbe described how, in *Frullania fragilifolia*, the large, flat antical lobe of the leaf would be shed as a propagule, leaving rows of the small postical lobes intact along the stems. These also could be induced to give rise to new plants. He grew them on sterile filter paper in Knop's solution in a Petri dish and obtained a cell mass at the cut surface after a few days. From this cell mass a young plant arose. According to him, the well-known deciduous perianth of *Gymnocolea inflata* is unique. Anybody familiar with this common plant of wet heaths will know how plentiful such perianths are. Acting as propagules, they must be an important factor making for the abundance of the species.

Cavers[40], in a useful summary of asexual reproduction and regeneration in Hepaticae, drew attention to a rather different process, intermediate between the two described above. It is well seen in thallose Marchantiales and consists of the production of 'adventive branches' (often from the underside of the midrib) and the subsequent breaking free of these to form new plants. Cavers noted how a whole pond surface could become covered by *Riccia fluitans* in this way, and how, in some xerophytic species of the same genus, tuberous branchlets thus released enabled the plants to survive periods of drought. He noted a similar process in *Targionia*, stating that 'the ventral shoots become detached at the base and form new plants'. This is comparable with the spread of a stoloniferous or rhizomatous vascular plant; no more than that, for there is little prospect of the new thallus being carried far by wind or water in the way that microscopic deciduous propagules could be.

It will now be convenient to consider some cases among mosses where the organ shed is a modified branch of bud-like form. This type of organ, which occurs in some species of *Bryum* and many species of *Pohlia*, is strictly a deciduous branchlet, although it is variously termed a 'gemma' or a 'bulbil' in taxonomic works. In *Bryum bicolor* var. *gracilentum* there is no mistaking the shoot-like character of the propagules, and the stem with its leaf rudiments may be lengthened to varying degrees. So, too, the 'bulbils' of *Pohlia bulbifera* and *P. rothii* are clearly foreshortened swollen axes with rudimentary foliar appendages. In the curious 'glove-shaped' propagules of *Pohlia annotina* the distinction between axis and leaf-like appendages is less clear; whilst the long, often vermiform and variously branched propagules of *Pohlia proligera* go a stage further. One is reminded of the strap-shaped 'protonema' of liverworts of the family Lejeuneaceae, some of which are described and figured by Fulford[74]. In each of the above species of *Pohlia* the form of the propagule constitutes an important taxonomic character. In the last two examples the propagules may be formed in great numbers, two to five normally per leaf axil in *P. annotina*, and more than five in *P. proligera*. They must be a principal means of propagation; yet in none of these species is the sporophyte unknown, although admittedly it is relatively rare.

We may now turn briefly to the general question of power of regeneration among bryophytes. The subject has important morphogenetic implications and, as Fulford[74] has shown in some detail, is closely linked with that of spore and gemma germination on account of the resemblances which often (but not always) obtain between stages in regeneration and the corresponding stages in sporeling and gemmaling in the same species. However, in the present context it will suffice to stress the extraordinarily well-developed powers of regeneration displayed by bryophytes and to indicate the relevance of this to the general topic of vegetative propagation.

Although Necker described experiments on regeneration as long ago as 1774 in his *Physiologia Muscorum*, it was not until the latter part of the nineteenth century that the subject attracted widespread attention, culminating in the reports of Vöchting[235], Schostakowitch[207] and Cavers[40]. Kreh[127] went on to explore the subject in a really comprehensive manner. In a long paper devoted to regeneration in liverworts he showed that almost every part of the plant, with the exception of antheridia, could be induced to undergo regeneration. He had success with isolated perianths, with archegonia, even with the ventral scales of Marchantiaceae and isolated rhizoid cells. In short, he was able to show how almost any organ or part of a liverwort plant which became severed from the parent body would be able, given suitable conditions, to regenerate in time a whole plant. The implications of this for vegetative spread are obvious. In fact Vöchting had already stated, for *Marchantia*, that every living cell is capable of regenerating the entire plant, and Goebel's statement that 'almost every living cell of a moss can grow out into protonema' carries a similar implication for mosses. Surely, no accident which can befall a clump of growing moss or liverwort (and result in fragmentation) will be without the possibility of beneficial consequences in the shape of subsequent spread. In more recent years Wettstein[254-6] and others have drawn on the truth of Goebel's dictum to encourage cut pieces of seta to form protonema and hence diploid gametophytes. Fulford[73-4] too has shown how the application of very dilute growth-promoting substances can greatly facilitate regeneration in hepatics. But the important inference remains for the present context, namely that bryophytes possess exceptional regenerative powers which cannot fail to be of use in propagation.

As already indicated, the term 'gemma' is used in a rather wide sense by some authors; but more properly it is restricted to a propagative organ of definite form and quite unlike the parent plant from which it springs. It characteristically originates from a single cell, but may be unicellular, bicellular or multicellular at the time of its release. It is not organized into a short axis and rudimentary leaves. If one accepts this last criterion one excludes the bulbils of most of the *Pohlia* species described above, but one retains many very diverse reproductive units that need not be catalogued in detail here. They include the large discoid gemmae of *Marchantia* and *Lunularia* which are so efficient that Goebel was able to say, with slight exaggeration, that they 'over-run every pot in cultivation'. They include a range of globose, discoid and plate-like structures of intermediate size, some being found in mosses, others in certain groups of liverworts; and a further group of units (found among mosses) whose filamentous form suggests derivation from protonema. Finally there is the great mass of leafy liverwort genera producing one- or two-celled gemmae on leaf points or modified stem apices. The masses of axillary structures formed in the moss *Isopterygium elegans* are probably better regarded as highly modified deciduous branchlets. Each consists of a length of tenuous stem bearing rudimentary leaves.

For the student wishing to study a small but reasonably representative range of these structures one might suggest the following: among liverworts, (1) the large discoid gemma of either *Lunularia* or *Marchantia*, (2) the small plate-like gemmae of *Metzgeria fruticulosa*, (3) *Blasia pusilla*—with two kinds of propagules, and (4) *Lophozia ventricosa* with its microscopic one- or two-celled gemmae; among mosses, (1) the fairly elaborate gemmae produced on highly characteristic receptacles in great numbers by either *Tetraphis pellucida* or *Aulacomnium androgynum*, (2) the microscopic filamentous gemmae of either *Ulota phyllantha* or *Orthotrichum lyellii*, and (3) ovoid or globose red or red-brown gemmae associated with the

D

rhizoid system, in either *Bryum erythrocarpum* or *Leptobryum pyriforme*. This would not involve any species which is particularly rare or difficult to obtain. A little may now be said about each.

The biconvex gemmae of the liverwort *Lunularia cruciata* are nearly 0·5 mm in diameter and are just visible to the naked eye. They are numerous in each receptacle (Fig. 14A) and gemmae of

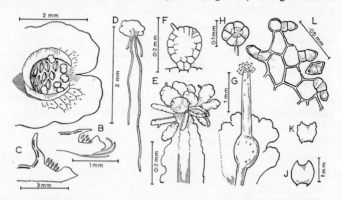

Fig. 14 Asexual reproduction in liverworts. A–D. *Lunularia cruciata*. A. Gemma receptacle, from above. B and C. Early and later stages, gemma receptacle in longitudinal section. D. Germinating gemma E–F. *Metzgeria fruticulosa*. E. Cluster of gemmae forming at extremity of thallus lobe. F. Single gemma. G–H. *Blasia pusilla*. G. Portion of thallus with flask-shaped gemma receptacle. H. single gemma. J–L. *Lophozia ventricosa*. J. Normal, and K. gemmiferous leaf. L. Gemmae arising from marginal cells of K, and one free gemma.

many different ages can be seen at any one time. When ripe they become readily detached from their short stalks, a process facilitated by the club-shaped mucilage hairs that occur on the receptacular surface. Close behind the apex of the thallus the gemmiferous receptacle becomes exposed by the raising of a flap of tissue on the upper surface of the thallus. Vertical longitudinal sections show that at first the receptacle is a deep hollow, almost concealed between the nearly vertical flap and the upturned apical part of the thallus. Later the receptacle is displaced backwards, the flap becomes a slope and the receptacular surface itself may be almost vertical. It is easy to see how this adjustment could assist in the washing away of the ripe gemmae. These structures, bright green and rich in starch and oil, have been described and figured again and again. They are remarkably similar in the two genera. It is worth examining the soil in the neighbourhood of gemmiferous plants in search of early stages in the germination of the gemmae. One may find one that has widened considerably by growth from both its laterally placed growing points and put forth a tuft of long slender rhizoids from the central 'cushion' (Fig. 14D).

Metzgeria fruticulosa is generally accorded specific rank nowadays, although it used to be classed as a variety of *M. furcata*. It is abundantly gemmiferous (Fig. 14E) and the branches which bear the gemmae are marked by narrow form and nearly erect growth. Gemma production in this genus has been well described by Evans[64]. *M. fruticulosa* is an abundant epiphyte in western Britain, and will repay careful study. Many stages in the origin of gemmae will be seen without difficulty. It will be noticed that each of the flat, roughly circular plate-like gemmae originates from a single superficial cell. Fully grown, the gemma (Fig. 14F) is about 0·2 mm in diameter. It does not exceed one cell layer in thickness and there is no marked differentiation of cells. However, at the pole remote from the attachment a distinct apical cell can usually be detected. Some marginal cells may grow out to form rhizoids even before the gemma is shed. This type of gemma resembles those described by Degenkolbe[57] for various members of the family Lejeuneaceae.

The propagules of *Blasia pusilla* have long been of interest to bryologists, for several reasons. First, this species has two perfectly distinct kinds of gemma; second, the production of one kind makes the plants extremely conspicuous; and third, the origin of the curious tubular or funnel-like organs responsible has been something of a mystery. Unfortunately, *Blasia* is not a common liverwort, but once found it is worth cultivating in the cool greenhouse, where it will grow successfully for a number of years. Plants grown at Reading, when first obtained from the field, bore many prominent tubular receptacles, with masses of the light green, subspherical gemmae collecting at the mouth of each tube, or funnel (Fig. 14G). Later they were replaced by the thin, angular gemmae which arise directly on the upper surface of the thallus. Mr P. J. Wanstall tells me he has had the same experience and suspects that the more constantly high humidity of the greenhouse may be responsible. Cavers[40] gave a careful description of the mode of origin of these two perfectly distinct kinds of gemma, and indicated how the swelling of mucilage hairs brings the spherical gemmae to the mouth of the funnel. These gemmae, on their long slender stalks, are akin to those found in the moss *Aulacomnium androgynum*, although their shape (Fig. 14H) is different. Those of the second type are scale-like. It has been suggested that the tubular receptacles of *Blasia* may be modified archegonial receptacles, on the evidence of occasional archegonia which have been found in them.

The gemmae of the leafy liverwort, *Lophozia ventricosa*, are among the simplest known, for they are one- to two-celled structures, usually the latter. They are formed in great numbers, either at each point of some of the bifid leaves or on the modified apical region of the axis. This type of gemma is widespread among leafy liverworts. When a leaf point becomes gemmiferous certain of the marginal cells begin to protrude, the walls concerned becoming clearly thinner than those of adjacent cells. After a time a transverse wall cuts off a stalk cell from what Degenkolbe terms a gemma mother cell. This mother cell may then proliferate in several directions (Fig. 14L), and as mature gemmae are released others arise beneath them. The process has been likened to conidial formation in certain fungi; and in the longitudinal section of a gemmiferous 'head' of *Calypogeia* figured by Cavers[40] the resemblance is certainly striking.

In *Lophozia ventricosa* it is usual for gemmae to become two-celled at a relatively late stage in development. Often a densely granular content distinguishes the gemmiferous cells from their neighbours. Degenkolbe[57] asserts that there is frequently a periodicity in gemma production, and he refers to the work of Buch[30] on species of *Scapania*. Sometimes the leaves bearing gemmae in *Lophozia ventricosa* are little altered in form, except that the two points bear clusters of these microscopic propagules; at other times they become erose and highly irregular in outline (Fig. 14K). Indeed, gemma production here seems to lack the precision that one associates with it where the gemmae are more complex.

Turning now to mosses, we may begin with *Tetraphis pellucida*, which is often abundant on decaying stumps. It grows in the form of a short turf, each of the crowded erect shoots ending in a peculiar cup formed of enlarged leaves. This terminal cup is the gemmiferous receptacle (Fig. 15A). When one dissects it into a drop of water

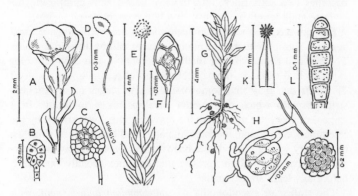

Fig. 15 Asexual reproduction in mosses. A–D. *Tetraphis pellucida*. A. Gemma 'cup'. B. young, and C. mature gemma (omitting lower part of stalk). D. Gemma with complete stalk. E–F. *Aulacomnium androgynum*. E. Stalk (pseudopodium) bearing gemmiferous head. F. Single gemma. G–J. *Bryum erythrocarpum*. G. Plant with globose gemmae on rhizoid system. H. Young gemma at grey stage. J. Mature gemma (crimson). K–L. *Ulota phyllantha*. K. Leaf, still young, with apical tuft of mature gemmae. L. Single gemma.

gemmae of varied age escape, perhaps twenty to thirty mature ones and many that are much younger. It is odd that these obviously immature stages should become detached so readily. Moreover, the same phenomenon is seen in *Aulacomnium androgynum*, where a parallel type of gemma occurs. In the latter species I have seen evident signs of germination in a gemma that was less than half the normal size and it is perhaps not essential that these gemmae complete their development in the receptacle.

In *Tetraphis*, at quite an early stage, most of the thirty-five to forty cells of the mature, roughly heart-shaped gemma are present.

The difference is in their smaller size and much less mature state. In very young stages (diameter $c.$ 25 μ) the cells are about 10 μ wide, with very delicate walls and minute plastids (Fig. 15B). The mature gemma (diameter $c.$ 150 μ) has cells about 20 μ wide (Fig. 15C), with firm walls and full-sized chloroplasts, although in the apical cell smaller plastids may be retained. Also, part of the central region becomes two cells thick, and the five or six cells composing the delicate stalk lengthen abruptly at a late stage in development.

Enough has been said to indicate that in the well-known gemma cups of *Tetraphis* there are many features calling for close study. There is still room here for further observation, and even more for experimental work. In the neighbourhood of gemmiferous plants of *Tetraphis* one may find some of the young stages of the thalloid structure into which the gemma develops on germination. In a stage that was little more than 0·5 mm in length I was struck by the resemblance, in shape, meristematic apex and basal tuft of rhizoids, to the very young plant of the brown alga, *Fucus*, figured by Newton[163]. Later the thalloid 'protonema' becomes broadly expanded, before any leafy shoots arise.

The stalks, or pseudopodia of *Aulacomnium androgynum*, with their terminal cluster of gemmae, appear like so many greenish pins (Fig. 15E) arising from the leafy shoots; this makes the species unique among British mosses, and it is very easily recognized. It grows on decaying stumps. In most essential features the gemmae resemble those of *Tetraphis*, although they differ in shape. Thus, they are borne on multicellular, delicately filamentous stalks, and the central part of the gemma (Fig. 15F) becomes two cells thick at maturity. The pattern of their germination, however, is quite different and a new leafy shoot arises relatively early.

Gemmae which consist of short filaments, composed of rather large, often relatively thick-walled cells, are not uncommon among epiphytic mosses. A striking example is *Ulota phyllantha*, where the gemmiferous surface is the projecting tip of the leaf (Fig. 15K,L). This moss is not confined to trees, but will also grow on rocks, often those near the sea and sometimes not far above high-water mark. While the leaf is still young, some of the cells in the shortly excurrnt. nerve grow out to form the filamentous, brownish-green gemmeae

Thus, leaf tips may appear fully mature and may bear the characteristic clusters of gemmae when the cells in the leaf base are scarcely
beyond the embryonic stage. Release is by the rupture of the basal
cell in the short filament and great numbers of broken cells can be
seen projecting from a leaf apex which has shed its gemmae. Gemmae of this kind form an efficient means of dispersal for a number
of epiphytic mosses and rather similar structures are seen in several
species of *Orthotrichum* and *Zygodon*. In most of these the gemmae
arise in variable numbers on the adaxial surface of the leaf. No case
is quite so striking as that of *Ulota phyllantha*, where the output of
gemmae from quite a small patch of the moss must be considerable.
It is perhaps significant that the sporophyte of *Ulota phyllantha* is
very rare indeed.

Quite different are the mosses which produce nearly spherical
gemmae on the rhizoid system. These are soil-dwelling species, and
there is no doubt that they owe to these gemmae much of their
success in colonizing bare patches of soil. A good example is *Bryum
erythrocarpum* (Fig. 15G), in the typical form of which the clusters of
cells so formed are indeed almost perfectly spherical. The ripe
gemmae (Fig. 15J) have projecting surface cells which remind one
of the drupels of a raspberry. They are also conspicuous on account
of their bright red colour. At this stage the gemmae are readily
detached and numerous 'scarlet balls' can commonly be seen lying
free about the bases of plants of this species, which is thus easily
identified*. A careful examination of the rhizoid system, however,
will reveal others that are still attached, whilst further gemmae will
be seen in various stages of development. In the early stages they
are grey in colour, and the cells thin-walled with dense granular
contents (Fig. 15H). Even then each consists of a solid 'knot' of
cells. The gemmae may be formed either on rhizoids springing from
the base of the stem or on others which develop in the axils of the
lower leaves. Each gemma appears to be the terminal swelling of a
short tertiary branch of the rhizoid system. The situation is a little
analogous to that of potato tubers.

Leptobryum pyriforme has ovoid gemmae on its rhizoid system.

*See Crundwell[54] for some hitherto overlooked species in the *B. ery-
throcarpum* complex.

They are of the same general character as those described above. Greenhouse pots are the favourite habitat of this moss; but another species where the importance of rhizoid gemmae has been claimed but apparently not reliably demonstrated is the very abundant and generally widespread moss *Ceratodon purpureus*.

It remains to touch on a few general matters relating to vegetative propagation in bryophytes. One is the question of distribution of gemmiferous species in the different major groups. A survey of the British bryophyte flora shows that species which produce true gemmae are quite unevenly distributed taxonomically. Thus, gemmae are found in under 10% of Marchantiales, in just under 20% of Metzgeriales, whilst nearly 40% of British Jungermanniales (leafy liverworts) are known to produce them. Correns[52], in the most comprehensive study ever made of gemma production in mosses, was able to refer to a surprising number of gemmiferous species, but he included every device for vegetative propagation, from specialized protonema branches to complete detachable shoots. Even so, it is unlikely that the proportion of British mosses so equipped exceeds 10%. The leafy liverworts are thus the group with the strongest tendency to form gemmae.

Turning to the question of the distribution of gemmiferous species by habitat, there seems little doubt that the conquest of two particular habitats by bryophytes has been associated with abundant and efficient gemma production. These are (1) the trunk, branches and leaves of trees, (2) soil surfaces, for example those of greenhouse pots, fallow fields and kindred habitats connected with the cultivation of the land by man. In moist, oceanic climates such as that of south-west Ireland, an abundance of bryophytes can be seen on the trunks and branches of trees. Species of leafy liverwort bulk large there, whilst among mosses genera such as *Zygodon*, *Orthotrichum* and *Ulota*, all with some gemmiferous species, are likely to be among the most prominent in positions high above the ground. Gemma production must be a factor in the success of some of these species, whilst others like *Ulota crispa* are widespread because they fruit freely. In parts of the humid tropics minute liverworts abound on the surfaces of large, long-persistent leaves of forest trees. These epiphyllous forms constitute a highly specialized group and nearly all are Jungermanniales. Again it might emerge that there was a positive correlation between the epiphyllous habit and the power to spread by gemmae.

The occurrence of *Marchantia polymorpha* and *Lunularia cruciata* as greenhouse weeds has already received mention. Their large output of gemmae is certainly a big factor in their success. The moss, *Leptobryum pyriforme*, another well-known weed of greenhouse pots, is doubly armed in that sporophytes usually abound but ovoid gemmae on the rhizoid system are commonly present too.

In the small but highly characteristic group of species that appear on the soil of fallow fields in late autumn and early winter one finds some that fruit freely, others that depend for their spread and persistence on efficient gemma or bulbil production. In the former category come various species of *Pottia* and *Barbula*; in the latter several species referable to the genus *Bryum*. Any device for rapid vegetative spread can scarcely fail to be advantageous in such a habitat.

As regards the agents of dispersal of gemmae, it is usually assumed that water is the most important: Brodie[24] has described a 'splash-cup' method of dispersal. Heavy rain must commonly be effective; but we may suppose that at various times the feet of animals and the wheels of vehicles will carry gemmae to new areas. Most types of gemma are unlikely to withstand drying, and wind will not therefore be important, except in areas of high humidity.

Enough has been said to show that vegetative propagation in bryophytes is a large and important topic. It is also one that has not lacked investigators, from the time of the classical morphological accounts to the modern period when the experimentalist is eager to make use of the special powers of bryophytes in this respect in his attempt to uncover some of the mechanisms of growth and differentiation. At the same time, we must not lose sight of the fact that in the basic life cycle of a bryophyte it is an entirely secondary phenomenon. The events which follow one another in unvarying alternation, generation after generation, in the lives of typical bryophytes are the union of gametes and the production of spores.

8

Sexual reproduction

AN IMPORTANT event in the life of the gametophyte is the appearance of sex organs. The male and female organs, termed respectively
antheridia and archegonia, are remarkably uniform in fundamental
structure throughout bryophytes. They are ordinarily provided with
some protection. The protective devices concerned, and the frequent
aggregation of sex organs in specialized parts of the plant body,
commonly render the fertile regions conspicuous, although the
essential organs are themselves microscopic.

The antheridium is a delicate sac enclosing antherozoid mother
cells and, ultimately, mature male gametes. In form it varies from
subglobose, through ovoid to ellipsoid; the wall of the sac is almost
always one layer of cells and the whole structure is borne on a stalk
of varying length. The antheridium invariably originates from a
single cell, normally superficial, but hypodermal in *Anthoceros*. A
primary stalk cell is cut off early, whilst rather later the body of the
antheridium differentiates as a result of periclinal cell divisions
which separate the wall from the interior mass of antherozoid
mother cells. Meanwhile the stalk region becomes multicellular.

In the Marchantiales, where these organs are sunk in characteristic chambers, the antheridium is ovoid, the stalk short and broad
(Fig. 16E). In Metzgeriales the form (cf. *Pellia* (Fig. 16A)) is more
nearly globose, but the stalk is still short. Typical leafy liverworts
(Jungermanniales), however, have antheridia borne in the axils of
concave leaves and the stalk is very long (Fig. 16D). Also, as
Parihar[173] points out for *Porella*, the wall may be locally two or
three layers of cells thick. Mature antheridia of *Sphagnum* (Fig. 16C)
resemble those of leafy liverworts in form, but those of Bryidae and
Polytrichidae are much longer and narrower than anything seen

among typical hepatics (cf. Fig. 16G,H). Each antheridium here grows for a considerable time by the activity of a clearly defined apical cell. Although the body of the antheridium is thus elongated the stalk remains short. These moss antheridia vary much in size. For example, typical antheridia of *Funaria hygrometrica* attain a length of 0·25 mm, those of *Polytrichum commune* 1·5 mm. Those of

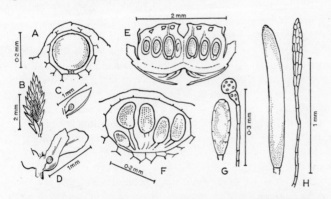

Fig. 16 The form of antheridia. A. *Pellia epiphylla* (in V.S. thallus). B–C. *Sphagnum rubellum*. B. Male branch. C. Antheridium with protective 'male bract'. D. *Diplophyllum albicans*. Part of male branch, with single 'male bract' and antheridium. E. *Reboulia hemispherica*, V.S. male receptacle. F. *Anthoceros* sp., group of antheridia in V.S. thallus. G. *Funaria hygrometrica*, antheridium and paraphysis. H. *Polytrichum* sp., antheridium and paraphysis.

Mnium hornum are intermediate between these two; whilst in plenty of mosses the antheridia are smaller than in *Funaria*.

The archegonium is often, and fairly aptly, described as flask-shaped. The essential parts are two, a wide rounded venter which houses the egg (female gamete) and ventral canal cell, and a long narrow neck. The whole structure is commonly borne on a short stalk. The neck is a tube enclosing a core of intensely protoplasmic neck canal cells. These, together with the ventral canal cell, break down to afford access to the egg. There is thus a single, non-motile female gamete, adequately protected in the hollow of the archegonial venter. It may be mentioned that the distinction between the

axial row of protoplasmic cells and the sterile wall cells is more
fundamental than is that between the broad, basin-shaped venter
and long, narrow neck.

Like the antheridium, the archegonium normally originates from
a single superficial cell, but again *Anthoceros* is exceptional in that
the resulting structure is not a free, elevated organ as it is in other
bryophytes. Instead, as we noted in Chapter 2, the wall of the archegonium is here confluent with surrounding thallus tissue and the
archegonium as a whole is remarkably small and short in the neck
(Fig. 17D). The neck canal cells are only four to six, whereas ten or
more neck canal cells occur in typical moss archegonia, and six to
eight in those of most other liverwort groups. Short archegonia,
with only four neck canal cells, are found, however, in some Marchantiales, for example *Riccia*, and in *Sphaerocarpos*. The separation
of the wall from the central part of the archegonium is an important
feature of early development, just as it is in the antheridium. The
distinctive features of the female organ become apparent only as
the venter enlarges to accommodate the big egg cell and the neck
lengthens sharply. Also, the central protoplasmic cells are always
few by comparison with the great number of antherozoid mother
cells in the antheridium. The stalk is lacking in *Anthoceros*, almost
so in *Riccia*. It is particularly long and massive in some of the
Bryidae (Fig. 17F). An apical cell governs archegonial development
in mosses as a whole, including *Andreaea* and *Sphagnum*, a fact
which makes for relatively elongated archegonia throughout the
class. Among liverworts, *Anthoceros* provides the single example of
markedly divergent archegonial structure. Otherwise, important
distinctions between one group and another seem to be few. In
general there are six rows of neck cells in Marchantiales, five in
Metzgeriales and Jungermanniales, and usually four in Calobryales.

We must now consider the morphological significance of the sex
organs. We have already noted that both archegonium and antheridium achieve their maximum in size and complexity in the bryophytes. It is usually thought that their long subsequent history has
been a path of gradual degeneration, with the antheridium ceasing
to be recognizable as such among the gymnosperms and the
archegonium persisting at that level, albeit in highly modified form.

Both organs, indeed, tend to be smaller and simpler in structure among pteridophytes than they are in bryophytes. In the latter it is only the small, short-necked archegonia of some thalloid liverworts that approach pteridophyte archegonial structure, one of the closest resemblances being between the embedded archegonium of *Anthoceros* and that of such a pteridophyte as *Selaginella*.

Thus, if these characteristic sex organs arose at bryophyte level

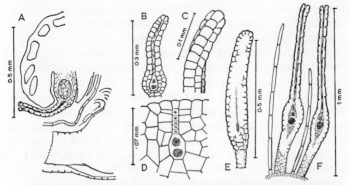

Fig. 17 Archegonia. A. *Preissia quadrata*. Part of V.S. young archegoniophore, with archegonium containing very young embryo. B–C. *Fossombronia angulosa*. B. Archegonium removed from apical part of thallus midrib, in optical section. C. Twisted neck of same, surface view. D. *Anthoceros sp.* V.S. superficial layers of thallus with immersed archegonium. E. *Hypum cupressiforme*. Abnormal sex organ, intermediate between antheridium and archegonium (found in female 'inflorescence' of plant from Gau Graig, Cader Idris, July 1949). F. *Bryum* sp. Two old archegonia, two paraphyses; note long stalks of archegonia.

it is clear that they quickly achieved their peak of structural elaboration. Perhaps this is to be expected in the one group of plants marked by dominance of the gametophyte generation; for we must never lose sight of the fact that the leafy shoot system and the thallus are here the haploid, gametophyte generation and hence in the strict sense of homology not to be compared with the vegetative body (root, stem and leaves) of vascular plants. Nevertheless the relatively sudden appearance, in the evolutionary sense, of a complex and

highly stereotyped organ such as the archegonium among bryophytes immediately poses the question of its origin. It would seem
reasonable to look among the algae for this.

Many have turned to the so-called plurilocular sporangia (in fact,
gametangia) of certain brown seaweeds as being likely to offer a
solution. Here, in such a genus as *Ectocarpus*, we find an ellipsoid
structure (in origin a single cell), which produces gametes that are
functionally either male or female. Apart from the possibility of a
significant difference in size between the two kinds of gametes produced, the two organs are alike; and to postulate them as the origin
of the archegonia and antheridia of bryophytes is to imply a common
origin for these two kinds of sex organ, notwithstanding the great
divergence that they demonstrate in every known bryophyte. Male
and female sex organs of contrasted form abound among the algae,
but the simple egg sac (or oogonium) which houses the non-motile
female gamete in such cases could not readily be transformed into
the flask-shaped archegonium of mosses and liverworts. It must be
remembered that in their young stages antheridia and archegonia
may be strikingly alike. This is especially so in the Calobryales.

Parihar in his textbook[173] has pursued the line of an origin from
plurilocular sporangia of certain brown algae, and has included
diagrams adapted from an early paper by Davis[55]. The transformation required for the antheridium is relatively moderate, being little
more than the acquisition of a delicate 'jacket' of sterile cells. That
required to make an archegonium from a plurilocular sporangium
is very much greater, and the argument is correspondingly less convincing there. The formation of a 'jacket' layer, a profound change
of form in the organ as a whole, and the pre-selection of a single
internal cell as the functional female gamete are all necessary.
Hence the gap is inherently difficult to bridge and morphologists have
been led to seek evidence of intermediates between archegonium
and antheridium. Such intermediates, it was thought, might not only
lend weight to the idea of a common origin, but might also demonstrate possible stages in the evolutionary history of these organs.

There has been no lack of observations on intermediate structures.
These go back at least to those of Lindberg on a species of *Hypnum*
in 1878. At intervals in the years that followed others were brought

to light, by Hy[109] in *Atrichum undulatum*, by de Bergevin[56] in *Plagiothecium silvaticum*, by Holferty[103] in *Mnium cuspidatum*. Bryan[26] reviewed the earlier literature and added his own striking observations on *Mnium medium*. In this synoecious species he found that each of two populations, situated sixty miles apart, had numerous abnormal organs intermediate in various ways between antheridia and archegonia. Bryan figured twenty of these. Some had what were clearly antherozoid mother cells within the stalk of an otherwise fairly normal archegonium. Others were substantially antheridia, but had an apparent egg and ventral canal cell amongst the mass of normal antherozoid mother cells. We now know that the usual haploid chromosome number in the genus *Mnium* is six, but that *M. medium*, in common with certain others, has the chromosome status n=12. It seems that polyploidy has here brought with it the situation in which the two kinds of sex organs are borne on a common receptacle. It is perhaps not surprising therefore that some intermediates should occur. They may be more frequent than is realized. I once came across what were obviously various intermediate types of sex organ (cf. Fig. 17E) when examining herbarium material of *Hypnum cupressiforme*. Bryan considered that such occurrences give ground for the belief that the two kinds of sex organ are homologous structures.

Haupt[96] in a study of the liverwort *Preissia quadrata* found that, although dioecism is the rule, about 1% of all plants seen were monoecious. Some monoecious plants carried bisexual receptacles in which there were a few abnormal, intermediate sex organs. Haupt figured an organ which looked as if it would have completed development as an egg-producing structure but which lay in a typical antheridial chamber. Again, on mainly female receptacles he found some undoubted antheridium-like structures. Haupt concluded that male and female receptacles of Marchantiales had had a common origin phylogenetically. He also drew the following conclusions regarding the nature of the sex organs themselves: (1) that canal cells are non-functional eggs, (2) that antheridia and archegonia are homologous organs, and (3) that the antherozoid mother cells are the equivalent (homologue) of the entire axial row of cells within the archegonium.

We will now turn to the arrangement and grouping of sex organs. In many genera of both mosses and liverworts dioecism is found and sometimes the separate male and female plants are widely different in size and appearance. We have seen this to be so in *Buxbaumia* among mosses, in *Sphaerocarpos* among liverworts, in both of which the male plants are minute. Quite often it would seem (cf. Gemmell[80]) that dioecism has given place to monoecism in the evolutionary history of a genus. Thus *Mnium medium* is a monoecious species in a genus where the majority are dioecious. Noguchi and Osada[165], in a recent review of the Japanese species of *Atrichum*, have revealed a similar situation, the majority of the species being dioecious with a haploid chromosome number of 7; but two varieties constitute exceptions, *A. undulatum* var. *undulatum* being monoecious (n=14) and *A. undulatum* var. *haussknechtii* actually having the sex organs together in a common inflorescence, the haploid chromosome number here being 21. A comparable situation exists elsewhere, for example in *Pohlia* and *Hypnum*, as indicated by Lewis[135] in an important paper which deals with some of the genetical implications of these facts. Lewis, citing Yano[265], also instances several species in which dioecious and monoecious strains are known. In each case the haploid chromosome number of the monoecious strain is double that of its dioecious counterpart. This suggests that monoecism is ordinarily a derived condition.

Where the two kinds of sex organs occur on the same plant they may develop in separate receptacles (loosely called inflorescences); the plant is then autoecious. In some monoecious species the apical cell cuts off antheridial initials closely followed by archegonial initials so that the two kinds of sex organ are separated only by one or two leaf insertions; this is the paroecious condition. Finally, in a synoecious species the two are intermingled in a common receptacle. For a long time differences in 'inflorescence' have formed an important criterion for the separation of closely related species in many groups of bryophytes. Thus, in the Eubryales, all except the paroecious condition are found in British species of *Bryum*, a genus that is notoriously difficult taxonomically; and all four conditions occur in *Pohlia*. Yet some species in these same genera are conceded to be variable in this respect, and in view of the evident link between inflorescence and cytology we have to admit that differences of this kind may be less fundamental than they were formerly thought to be.

Some interest attaches to the arrangement of antheridia, especially since there is wide disparity here between different groups of bryophytes. There is a great difference, for instance, between the liverwort *Riccia*, in which antheridia appear singly, scattered along the median line of the thallus, and such mosses as *Funaria, Polytrichum* and others, where there is a highly organized grouping of antheridia and associated paraphyses. The latter would seem to convey advantages and represent a derived state.

Thalloid and leafy plant bodies, however, pose two quite different problems in this matter. In thalloid liverworts the sinking of antheridia in pits or chambers not only provides efficient protection but may also allow for a mechanism of quite violent discharge of antherozoids. This is well seen in the antheridial chambers which form a series of radiating lines in the stalked male receptacles of *Marchantia polymorpha*. At the time of discharge the wall cells of the antheridium become distended and their abutment against the walls of the chamber brings pressure to bear on the contained mass of antherozoids. The key to the process lies in the formation of abundant mucilage; also in the differentiation of a cap cell (or group of cells) which bursts to release the male gametes. Cavers[39] pointed out that in *Conocephalum conicum* this discharge was explosive, the antheridial content escaping in the form of fine jets capable of reaching a height of over 5 cm. In *Conocephalum* the antheridia are grouped in discoid male receptacles sharply differentiated from the vegetative thallus. A measure of grouping of antheridia is also attained in various thalloid genera of the Metzgeriales (see also Chapter 2). *Anthoceros*, however, is unusual in that each individual chamber commonly contain two to five antheridia, and sometimes many more (Proskauer[186]). In the often tiered wall cells of the antheridium in *Anthoceros*, moreover, green plastids are conspicuous. Later they become orange, and colourful patches marking male receptacles are then obvious to the naked eye. A similar sequence of pigmentation is not uncommon in the wall (jacket) cells of moss antheridia (cf. *Funaria*).

In the Jungermanniales (leafy liverworts) the long-stalked, sub-globose antheridia are usually borne singly in the axils of specialized concave leaves, the whole male shoot often being catkin-like in form and noticeably different from one that is purely vegetative. The exceptional size of these catkin-like male shoots may be a useful specific character, as it is for example in the bog liverwort, *Cephalozia macrostachya*. A similar arrangement exists in *Sphagnum*, where the catkinate male branches are often conspicuous too for their highly coloured leaves (Fig. 16B). In all these examples the protection of the antheridium is only such as can be conveyed by the concavity and close proximity of the leaves (male bracts) concerned.

In *Funaria hygrometrica* (Bryidae), the antheridia are densely packed in a male receptacle where the sterile hairs, or paraphyses, have also an important part to play. Antheridia may be found in many stages of development and a single receptacle of *Funaria hygrometrica* is thus probably capable of releasing a succession of viable male gametes over a period of at least several weeks. It is easy to appreciate how the paraphyses in this species, with their swollen sub-spherical terminal cells (Fig. 16G), can be of value in protection, moisture conservation, building up pressure to make possible efficient discharge of antherozoids, and (to a limited extent) in photosynthesis. The terminal cells of the paraphyses meet over the antheridia. Both terminal and subterminal cells are rich in chloroplasts. Lorch[138] considered that their principal significance lay in conserving moisture around the antheridia.

Paraphyses usually form simple filaments which reach their broadest point above the middle, though not always (as in *Funaria*) in the terminal cell itself. Also, I have examined paraphyses in *Mnium*, *Bryum*, *Pohlia*, *Philonotis* and other genera without finding any that are as richly chlorophyllose as those of *Funaria hygrometrica*. In *Polytrichum* some of the paraphyses are more elaborate, being several cells wide in their broadest part (Fig. 16H). Always the longest paraphyses seem to overtop the antheridia so that the essential organs are in a sense embedded. Sometimes, e.g. *Philonotis*, the special form of associated leaves (perigonial bracts) makes for additional protection and the whole mass of antheridia and paraphyses may appear as if sunk in a kind of hollow. The antheridia in such a cluster may number several hundred.

It has sometimes been suggested that more use might be made of paraphysis struct ure as a taxonomic character, but it is seldom that really clear-cut differences exist between the paraphyses of two closely related species. Dixon[58] emphasized how valuable this character can be in separating non-fruiting plants of *Splachnum sphaericum* and *Tetraplodon wormskjoldii*, but even here there are other readily seen differences.

In most mosses antheridial production ultimately uses up the apical cell, but *Polytrichum* is an exception. Here proliferation through the old antheridial receptacle is well known, and I have seen examples in which several successive years' male receptacles have arisen at short intervals in this manner.

The position and arrangement of archegonia, being bound up with the subsequent development and fate of the sporogonium, have already received some attention. The simple thalloid liverwort *Riccia* bears its archegonia singly, and embedded in the thallus at maturity. Small groups are found in *Corsinia* and *Targionia*, and on the mushroom-shaped archegoniophores of the higher Marchantiales archegonia are grouped to varying extents. As Smith[218] points out, quite early in development the archegonia are displaced from the upper to the lower surface of the 'mushroom head' (cf. Fig. 17A). In the highly specialized *Marchantia polymorpha* there is a regular sequence of development in each radial line of archegonia, the youngest being nearest to the stalk. In contrast with this high degree of organization, the archegonia in *Sphaerocarpos* are produced singly on the upper surface of the thallus. They are not embedded, but the characteristic involucre (pear-shaped in some species) provides the necessary protection. Again, in the immersed archegonia of *Anthoceros* we find no organization into groups; but in most other bryophytes several of these organs arise in quick succession so that the receptacle will ultimately offer a cluster of archegonia for fertilization by male gametes. According to Smith[218], in some Jungermanniales only one archegonium is formed at a shoot apex, but in this order and in the Metzgeriales more are the rule. In *Sphagnum* there are typically three in a group, whilst in the Bryidae considerably larger groups are usual. Wherever specialized protective structures are involved, 'bracts' and perianth of leafy liverworts, perichaetial leaves of mosses and so on, it would seem advantageous to have the archegonia in clusters, and this can probably be regarded as a derived condition. In leafy liverworts and mosses the formation of archegonia normally ends the growth of the branch concerned. In acrocarpous mosses this happens on a principal long shoot; in pleurocarpous mosses on a short lateral one.

Two special features distinguish archegonia in which the ovum (or egg cell) is ready for fertilization. One is the breakdown into a swelling slimy mass of the neck canal cells and ventral canal cell, with the consequent separation of the cover cells. The other is the secretion of special chemical compounds which serve to bring the motile male gametes not only to the neck of the archegonium but down the narrow passage that leads to the egg. According to Parihar[173], the secretion in *Riccia* may consist of proteins and inorganic salts of potassium. The same author implies that most other bryophytes display a similar mechanism, but there seems to be little precise information. Various authors have stated that cane sugar is the active substance in the moss *Funaria*. Showalter[214] pointed out that in *Riccardia* the disorganized canal cells were not responsible for the secretion, although some modern authors (cf. Parihar[173]) continue to imply that they are, at any rate in most bryophytes.

As with chemotactic phenomena, so with the operation of water as the chief agency of transfer of male gametes, careful observations by earlier botanists have supplied much of the information on which modern accounts rest. Where the two kinds of sex organ lie near one another the onset of wet conditions would seem sufficient. In the water thus supplied motile male gametes could reach the necks of archegonia. In some monoecious and all dioecious species, where male and female receptacles may be widely separated, rain splash and the visits of microscopic animals such as mites have been recorded as mechanisms of transfer. Considerable light, however, was thrown on the whole subject by the researches of Muggoch and Walton[158]. These authors referred to the earlier observation of

Showalter[213] that if a large number of antherozoids (of *Riccardia pinguis*) were placed at one end of a small pool of water 1 cm long by 0·5 cm wide, nearly all remained crowded at that end of the pool an hour later. Hence one must not lean too heavily on the swimming powers of the motile male gamete. Moreover, Muggoch and Walton remind us that it is usual for antherozoids to leave the antheridium in a compact mass, still enclosed within their mother cells. Even in *Conocephalum* the male gametes are still within delicate membranes when they are ejected in violent spurts.

The important contribution of the above authors was to indicate the great part played by an intermediate stage in the process, a stage taking place after the release of the mass of 'sperm cells' and before the onset of the free-swimming life of the male gamete. They found that in most bryophytes investigated the arrival of the mass at the surface of the water resulted in immediate and rapid spreading. This was caused by some substance capable of drastically lowering surface tension. Fat was probably responsible, for this was detected within the antheridia of all species showing this phenomenon but was lacking in *Conocephalum* and *Sphagnum*, the two which gave negative results. In a later note Walton[240] pointed out that in *Pellia epiphylla* only fifteen seconds were required for the surface spreading, but a further fifteen minutes might elapse before the free-swimming antherozoids were fully released from their mother cells. By means of this important mechanism they had already been conveyed almost to the necks of the archegonia.

We may now examine the final stages of development of the cells within the antheridium. The terminology adopted by Smith[218] and Parihar[173] is not wholly satisfactory, since it results in the term 'androcyte' being used for something different from the 'spermatocyte' of Muggoch and Walton[158]. It is better for our purpose to avoid unnecessary terminology. In all nearly mature antheridia there are numerous small cubical cells. The last generation of these are the mother cells of male gametes. Original figures by Ikeno[110] for *Marchantia polymorpha* and by Black[15] for *Riccia frostii* (widely copied since) imply that in these forms the contents of each mother cell then divide diagonally into two, without the formation of a cell wall. Each resulting unit (androcyte of Smith) then transforms directly into a male gamete. The same happens in *Pellia* and perhaps in most liverworts, but the diagonal division of the mother cell into two is not found in mosses (cf. Wilson[262]).

Parihar[173] has summarized the transformation of androcytes into antherozoids in *Riccia*, basing his remarks and figures on the work of Black[15] on *R. frostii*. He notes the following: (1) a change of shape, the androcyte becoming first rounded, then comma-shaped, and finally elongated and closely coiled as it assumes the form of an antherozoid; (2) the emergence of an extra-nuclear body, the blepharoplast, which becomes increasingly long and narrow, but is finally thickened at one end—the head of the antherozoid; (3) a change in the shape of the nucleus, which also becomes homogeneous; and (4) the emergence of two long flagella which by their lashing give the antherozoid its power of movement. An entirely new light has been thrown on the final structure, however, by electron microscope studies of the male gametes in a number of bryophytes.

Manton and Clarke[149] were the first to reveal unsuspected complexities in the male gametes of the bog-moss *Sphagnum*, and among other things they deduced the eleven-strand composition of the flagella. Manton[148] subsequently proved this eleven-strand structure by means of a brilliant series of electron micrographs depicting sectioned male gametes. She was also able to discuss many other details, some of them highly specialized. Suffice it to emphasize that a whole new field of sub-microscopic structural detail is here opened up, in which it is likely that further work will reveal important morphological differences between different groups. Sato[203], also using the electron miscroscope, has already alluded to the peculiar dumb-bell-shaped body of the antherozoid in *Anthoceros* and to the existence, in all the eight bryophytes examined by him, of a hitherto undetected structure which he has called the filamentous appendage. Manton[148], who refers to it as a fibrous band, thinks it may help to convey structural stability to the cell. It is closely connected with both flagella and nucleus.

Hence we now have a much more detailed picture than ever before of those actively motile, microscopic structures, the male gametes, which effect fertilization in mosses and liverworts. In examining living material it is often possible to see them for oneself. In *Funaria hygrometrica*, for example, one may observe the gradual extrusion of the greyish mass of mother cells, and (under a higher magnification) something of the coiled form and rapid movements of the male gametes themselves.

Union of the antherozoid nucleus with that of the ovum completes the process of fertilization. Andersen[5] has commented that in diameter the egg nucleus is almost always about twice that of the antherozoid. Haupt[96], among others, has indicated that the actual union of the two nuclei may be only gradually achieved. Thereafter one is concerned with events in the new sporophyte generation, and it remains only to remark briefly on the fate of other archegonia. In all ordinary cases the successful fertilization of one archegonium implies the loss of function of those that remain. Sometimes, after gametophyte tissue has grown to accommodate the increasing bulk of the sporophyte, these abortive archegonia may be seen in odd positions. In certain species of moss, however, multiple fertilizations are normal and two or more sporophytes arise within a single cluster of perichaetial leaves. *Dicranum majus* affords a good example, in which Sowter[219] found that the commonest number was two, but it could be as high as six. I have seen seven perfectly normal sporophytes springing from a single perichaetium in *Mnium undulatum*. Longton[137] has just given a useful survey of this condition in British bryophytes. Entirely different again are the cases reported from time to time (Gyorffy[92], Watson[242]) where a single fertilization takes place but, owing to subsequent abnormal behaviour of the apical region of the young sporophyte, a monstrosity results and two capsules stand firmly united at the tip of a single seta.

9

Morphogenesis; anatomy; physiology

THE three approaches to the study of bryophytes which are to be considered in this chapter are all necessary for the fuller understanding of the living plant. Starting from different standpoints and employing diverse techniques, they converge in throwing light on the development and functioning of the plant as a whole. Morphogenesis emphasizes the unfolding of the structural pattern and seeks to understand the causes which promote the onset of each new phase in development. Thus attention comes to be focussed on certain stages, for example the onset of bud formation on the protonema of a moss or the first signs of differentiation in the very young sporophyte. A grasp of bryophyte anatomy is essential because it is only in terms of anatomical structure that the developmental changes can be observed and followed. Furthermore, the structural adaptations revealed may well provide clues to physiological processes. Finally, the more important physiological activities of bryophytes are today being submitted to the rigours of precise experimental study. Hence the decision to include some review of these three big topics in a single chapter. Thereby we may be enabled to understand more clearly what follows in Chapter 10 under the head of bryophyte ecology.

First we must examine the very young stages of bryophytes, which are seen immediately after the germination of spores. Fulford, besides giving accounts of certain chosen examples, has ably reviewed the position as a whole in the leafy liverworts[74]. She points out that as long ago as 1862 Hofmeister recognized three distinct patterns of early development among liverwort sporelings. Leitgeb[132] extended these to four, whilst Goebel[85] was the first to describe some of the distinctive patterns found in the family Lejeuneaceae. Fulford[74], who has added much to our knowledge of this field, recognizes ten structural patterns of the first phase after spore germination. These, with genera exemplifying them, are: the filamentous type of *Cephalozia*, the cell body of *Nardia*, the disc of cells found in *Radula* and the ball of cells found in *Frullania*; these being followed by a further six patterns prevailing in different members of the Lejeuneaceae. This phase ends with the cutting out of a three-sided apical cell; but two further stages intervene before the appearance of stem and leaves of adult form. These are (1) the shoot with primary leaves (which may be unicellular, may consist of a cell row, or may be broader at the base) and (2) the shoot with juvenile leaves, which may in varying degrees approach the form of adult leaves.

The early development of the gametophyte in leafy liverworts is thus a process of several stages, with different patterns prevailing in different groups. There seems to be a relationship between these patterns and the systematic affinities that have been determined, on other grounds, for the plants concerned. Chalaud[44,46] experimented with applications of various nutrients and succeeded in inducing many kinds of variation. Fulford maintains, however, that there is always an underlying pattern of development which is constant for any particular genus and is probably also constant, within limits, throughout a family.

Where the adult form is a thallus the early stages are on the whole more contracted, and events proceed more directly towards the final end to be achieved. This is well seen in *Pellia epiphylla* where a multicellular stage is attained even before the rupture of the spore wall. Polarity is early acquired and the basal cell may often be distinguished by its less dense protoplasm and few chloroplasts. From this basal cell the first rhizoid grows out, and soon a functional apical cell is cut out at the opposite pole of the young plant. Clapp[48] traced the corresponding events in *Riccardia pinguis* and in no really fundamental feature do these differ from those in *Pellia*. The spore is markedly enlarged at the onset of germination and the first cell walls are formed before the spore coat is ruptured. There is the same early attainment of polarity and a rather similar, roughly ovoid cell mass eventuates.

The early stages of the gametophyte in the Marchantiales have been investigated by O'Hanlon[169], Menge[153] and others. More recently, Mehra and Kachroo[152] have examined members of the Rebouliaceae and Kachroo[121] has described the early development of *Targionia hypophylla*. In the latter he recognizes four stages: (1) the emergence of a germ papilla; (2) the formation of a row of cells, the germ tube; (3) expansion of this into a germ plate; and (4) the germ disc in which the apical cell is ultimately cut out. Here, then, is a filamentous young stage, albeit one that is quickly superseded; and Kachroo remarks that secondary filamentous germ tubes may form in conditions of feeble illumination, just as they do in the Rebouliaceae. It would seem that in these thalloid forms, as in the leafy liverworts, there is an underlying pattern of development but some plasticity in the face of unusual conditions.

Among mosses thalloid juvenile stages are rare, and most commonly a filamentous phase (the protonema) gives place ultimately, and abruptly, to the leafy shoot system of the gametophore. Reference has been made earlier to the so-called thalloid protonema of *Sphagnum*, *Andreaea* and a few others, and we need not dwell on these exceptional cases here. Instead we will consider some recent work on the freely branched filamentous protonema of ordinary mosses. *Funaria hygrometrica* has been a frequent subject of study. The principal aims have been to distinguish successive developmental phases, and to suggest if possible what mechanisms control the onset of each new phase. This is the special province of the experimental morphologist, who must also often be something of a physiologist as well. Unfortunately, there is as yet no full agreement as to the stages in protonemal development to be recognized, and this despite much critical work by investigators in several countries.

The central controversy concerns the question as to whether, in such a moss as *Funaria hygrometrica*, one can recognize two clear-cut stages in protonemal life and form, the stages that have been named chloronema and caulonema. This idea of a clear two-phase development was put forward by Sironval[216] and has since been strongly supported by Bopp[18]. The latter author lists six morphological characters in which the first-formed chloronema differs from the caulonema which succeeds it. Among other things, the chlor-onema shows irregular branching, no oblique cross walls, colourless cell-walls in general and numerous, evenly distributed chloroplasts which are mostly nearly circular in outline. At a certain stage (after about twenty days according to Sironval) this is succeeded by caulonema, which Bopp distinguishes by its very regular lateral branches, oblique cross walls, a tendency for cell walls to be brown-ish and chloroplasts fewer, spindle-shaped and less evenly dis-tributed. He adds two further differences concerning the nuclei. In a subsequent important review of many aspects of morphogenesis in mosses Bopp[19] has upheld his verdict that these two phases are truly distinct. Moreover, it is only on branches of caulonema that buds can be formed.

Clearly, if this is true, a study of the conditions controlling the onset of caulonema will be important; and in this connection Bopp has pointed out that low temperature, submersion and low light intensity may each independently delay or prevent the establish-ment of caulonema, and hence of buds. The quality of light is also said to be important. Bopp goes on to explain that these two phases differ physiologically. Caulonema, unlike its forerunner, will show a negative response to unilateral illumination; and two unconnected caulonema branches growing adjacent to one another were found to impede each other's growth, as the result of an unknown inhibitor being secreted. Bopp claims to have recognized these two phases in other genera, for example in *Fissidens*, *Barbula*, *Splachnum* and *Bryum*. He believes that the two decisive facts which prove caul-onema to be a distinct stage of differentiation are (1) that it requires definite conditions for its appearance, and (2) that its physiological reactions are different from those of chloronema.

Both van Andel[233] and Allsopp and Mitra[3] have been unable to confirm the above interpretation of protonema as consisting of two clear-cut phases. Even Kofler[125], in her exceedingly thorough inves-tigation of the early gametophyte stages of *Funaria hygrometrica in vitro*, remained very imperfectly convinced. This is no doubt partly because protonema is both subject to considerable genetic variation and also highly plastic in its reaction to different environmental conditions. Kofler indeed claims that protonema brings out genetic differences more strongly than do the gametophore and sporophyte, where the environment has had more time in which to exert an effect. Concerning plasticity, Bopp found that if isolated cells (or short fragments) of caulonema were taken apart, they grew but reverted to chloronema. Kofler found that the presence of ammonium nitrate resulted in a slower protonemal growth throughout, and an abrupt falling off altogether after about three weeks. She found other factors, including impurities in the agar, which could exert an influence.

Whatever our views on the controversial matter of chloronema and caulonema, the crucial point in protonemal development will always remain that of bud initiation, with the formation of a tetrahedral apical cell. It is therefore not surprising that in recent years many workers have focussed attention on the effect that varying experimental conditions may have on this point. Two examples may be cited, that of Gorton and Eakin[86] in America and that of Mitra and Allsopp[156] in Britain.

Gorton and Eakin[86] found evidence of an unknown inhibitor, which prevented further elongation of protonemal filaments after a certain stage had been reached. They saw this stage as closely connected with the onset of bud formation, for which, however, they considered that two further factors were important (1) the building up of an adequate nutrient store and (2) the supply of certain growth substances. They worked on *Tortella caespitosa*. Mitra and Allsopp[156] (partly in collaboration with Wareing[157]), studying *Pohlia nutans*, concluded that, although a certain minimum concentration of sugar in the protonema may be essential for bud formation, it is probable that some more specific substance, synthesized by protonema only in the light, is required. Red light seemed to be necessary, but subsequent experiments with physiologically active substances suggested that kinetin or gibberellic acid might replace it, in part at least, in whatever essential but unexplained role it was playing. When the buds arise they do so normally on the periphery and their appearance has been likened to a 'fairy ring'. In certain genera (e.g. *Polytrichum* spp., *Trematodon*) they are said by Bopp to be more evenly distributed.

The studies of Meusel[154] have shown that even when the first

leafy shoots have grown from the initial crop of buds the gametophyte is still far from mature. Several successions of immature
leafy shoots ordinarily follow before shoots bearing sex organs are
produced. Thus, the position is perhaps not very different from that
already outlined for leafy liverworts; but there the successive phases
are more minute and more rapidly phssed through. Reflecting on
Meusel's observations of the first-formed leafy shoots in mosses,
one feels that they have not received all the attention that they merit.
There is even the possibility that some of the taxonomist's 'varieties'
may be referable to immature states of a species.

Eventually shoots will arise which are capable of bearing sex
organs; and thence will follow the sporophyte which presents its
own riddles to the experimental morphologist. One of the special
merits of Bopp's recent masterly contribution to this whole subject[19]
is that he not only reviews all gametophyte stages, but goes on to
seek the forces at work in the development of the new sporophyte
generation. He examines each stage in the light of recent experimental studies. Often there appear to be systems involving the precise co-ordination of stimulating and inhibitory substances. As Bopp
remarks, however, we are still far from knowing what determines
the formation of the utterly different structure of the sporophyte as
such, as soon as fertilization has been effected. It is certainly not
the fact of diploidy. Again, even when a mechanism is detected, the
exact nature of the substances responsible often eludes us.

At the outset, Bopp emphasizes the three crucial stages in the
development of a moss. These are (1) spore germination and the
development of filamentous protonema; (2) formation of a three-
sided apical cell and the origin from this of the gametophores (leafy
shoots), followed in turn by sex organs; (3) fertilization and the subsequent development of the sporophyte. We have seen that much in
the first stage remains at present controversial. According to Bopp,
the later part of the second stage is marked by a kind of apical
dominance. Inactivation of the shoot apex, artificially or in nature,
results in the unfolding of side branches. An indole-acetic acid—
kinetin antagonism—has been named as a mechanism, and on this
the experiments of MacQuarrie and Maltzahn[143] are illuminating.
In the third stage, as Bopp points out, it is hard to assess the relative

roles of the sporophyte itself, the gametophyte shoot that supports it and the covering organ or calyptra. One clear fact emerging is that, although the apophysis (neck) is commonly the first part of the sporophyte to swell, the apical regions are normally the first to begin development, and they act as a kind of 'organizer' for the rest. A capsule with its tip removed has its subsequent development much impaired.

Possibly the most striking fact of all, which Bopp duly emphasizes, is the importance of the intact calyptra as a control. That the calyptra had some part to play more than as a mere protection has been increasingly appreciated ever since the early work of Zielinski[267] and Herzfelder[97]. Bopp himself[17] and others have shown conclusively that premature removal of the calyptra results, in different cases, in a rapid increase in the number of cell divisions or in the volume of the new cells formed, or in both. There follows premature swelling of an imperfectly mature capsule and the formation of a poorly differentiated monstrosity.

We have been concerned in the last few pages with morphogenesis, a study which focusses our attention on the plant as a whole. Yet many of its observations have to be made on cells and tissues, whilst the processes studied are physiological. Hence it is fitting now to turn to some features of bryophyte anatomy, examining these where possible in relation to the facts of physiology. It will be necessary to confine the discussion to certain selected topics.

The bryological anatomist has first to remind himself that in the stems and leaves of mosses, and in the tissues which they display, he is dealing with structures that have no direct counterpart in vascular plants. He is, in a word, examining gametophyte structures, whereas the whole organized anatomical structure of pteridophytes and seed plants, including vascular bundles, woodiness and the rest, has taken place in the sporophyte. If we are to look among bryophytes for the strict counterpart (or homologue) of these features, then we must look in capsule, seta and foot. Anything found in the gametophyte will be at most a parallel development. We do indeed find, among the larger gametophytes of mosses and liverworts, quite a complex tissue differentiation. In the best-developed sporophytes (cf. *Anthoceros*, *Funaria*, etc.) we find epidermis, stomata, water-storage tissue, chlorophyllous tissue and some kind of conducting parenchyma; but of genuine vascular strands, as understood among higher plants, we find no trace whatever. Spiral thickenings in columella cells of *Dendroceros crispus* have, however, been noted by Proskauer[188a].

Lorch, in his very full account of the anatomy of mosses[138], alludes to the central strand that is sometimes, but not always, present in the foot. He also shows that the seta can at times display marked tissue differentiation. This is so, for example, in the Australian moss *Dawsonia polytrichoides*, the seta of which Lorch figures in transverse section. Around a well-developed central strand this seta has a sheath of cells strongly suggestive of endodermis. The seta is often notable for the number of thick-walled cells in its composition, especially near the surface, where for mechanical reasons they are most needed. Thick walls are found too in the epidermal cells of the capsule (exothecial cells); but according to Lorch these always remain unlignified. If woodiness is absent, however, cutinization is apparently widespread on the surfaces of these organs. Lorch quotes the earlier work of Strunk[223] on the widespread occurrence of cuticle in mosses, and some kind of cuticular covering is probably responsible for the high gloss normally seen on seta and capsule. Without it the green capsule would be very vulnerable to desiccation.

Of greater ecological significance, because operative throughout the life of moss or liverwort, are the anatomical features of the gametophyte. Here again the incidence of cuticle is of interest. Buch[31] has shown that, on the whole, a delicate but perceptible cuticle is present on the leaves of those mosses in which the main water supply comes from below. In these, of which the genera *Bryum* and *Mnium* are good examples, the rhizoids are used to some extent to extract water from the substratum and it is then conducted up the stems to the leaves. They are called endohydric mosses. On the other hand, there are many mosses in which no cuticle can be demonstrated, and here the normal water supply is from above. In these instances the leaves often recover from the curled-up state remarkably quickly when they are supplied with water. Well-known examples are species of *Trichostomum*, *Tortella*, *Orthotrichum* and *Ulota*. They are called ectohydric. A further group, combining in some measure the characteristics of these two, is said to be mixohydric. The same division can be made among liverworts: most Marchantiales are endohydric, whilst leafy liverworts are mainly ectohydric.

It is clear that we have here two biologically contrasted groups that are likely to differ from one another in other anatomical characters. They might be expected to have very different development of tissues specialized for the conduction of water. Before examining this point, however, we must enquire what is known of the physiology of water conduction in bryophytes.

Mägdefrau[145] established some important conclusions, among them the fact that both external and internal water conduction are important. External conduction takes place in capillary channels related to the form and arrangement of leaves. The wider the angle at which leaves stand out from the stem the less will be this capillary conduction. Also, it will naturally tend to diminish with wider separation of the leaves on the stem. Mägdefrau considered that the methods used by Bowen[21-2] did not allow reliable conclusions to be drawn from her work. Internal conduction is prevailingly in the central strand. Mägdefrau found that at 90% relative humidity internal conduction alone sufficed to maintain turgescence in leafy shoots. At lower relative humidities it was unable to do so for most mosses, and both types of conduction were necessary.

More recently Zacherl[266] has made an important contribution to this subject. He used fluorescent dyes to trace the path of internal conduction in selected mosses. He found that in such genera as *Mnium* internal conduction was in the central strand of the stem and in the leaf midrib. The leaf lamina and the ground tissue of the stem were secondarily supplied from these sources. In such cases the differentiated tissues of the leaf midrib do not link up with the central strand of the stem, but end blindly in the ground tissue forming so-called 'false leaf traces'. According to Zacherl these act after the manner of wicks, and the passage of water from the central strand of the stem to the leaf base is thereby accomplished across the intervening ground tissue. In such a genus as *Polytrichum*, by contrast, true leaf traces are continuous from the central strand of the stem out into the midribs of leaves (Fig. 18D). Here internal conduction is localized throughout in these specialized tissues. Zacherl adds that conduction of water by way of the central strand of a stem is most rapid and direct to the uppermost leaves, and that the lower leaves are as a result often satisfied later than the shoot tips. In moss stems in which a central strand is either feebly developed or absent he holds that there is no internal conduction.

Finally, mention may be made of the work of Bopp and Stehle[20] on the flow of water in the moss *Funaria hygrometrica*, with special reference to the path of supply from gametophyte to sporophyte. Fluorescent dyes were again employed. These authors found that this species was truly a mixohydric moss, for conduction through the gametophyte was by a combination of internal and external pathways. Internal conduction in rhizoids, for example, was found to be slow (ten cells traversed in forty hours), and the stem base seems normally to be reached much more rapidly by an external capillary path. Once the water is in the stem, however, the central strand is found to be important; but access to the leaves is more commonly by external channels.

On the subject of supply to the sporophyte these authors point out that the haustorial (sucker-like) base of the foot is plunged deep in the tissue of the gametophyte central strand, which ensheaths it 'beaker-wise'. A narrow intercellular space separates these two tissues. Experiments with fluorescent dyes showed that this intercellular space jacket was coloured before the extremity of the central strand and before the tip of the haustorium; whereafter ascent was rapid by way of this 'internal capillary channel'. Within the sporophyte the central strand of the seta was important for conduction. The calyptra acted as a kind of 'transpiration shield', and its removal led to a more rapid upward flow of the experimental fluid. It would be of interest to see the results of further experiments of this kind, on other species of moss. Bopp and Stehle have indicated that, for one species at least, the relationship between external and internal water conduction may be far from simple. Each is significant at different stages.

It remains to examine the extent of tissue specialization in the

E

central strands of stems and the midribs of leaves. *Polytrichum commune* or *P. formosum* (Fig. 18E) will provide excellent illustrations of a high degree of such differentiation in the stem. The central tissue consists chiefly of groups of relatively large cells, the hadrom of many authors. This is surrounded by a tissue composed of smaller cells with thinner walls. It has commonly been known as leptom, although different authors have given different names to it, some seeing the outermost layers of this zone as a distinct sheath, composed of starch-filled cells. Outside this is a wide cortical zone that is green in the young stem and passes over into the peripheral layers which are marked by very thick-walled cells. One can detect patches of colourless hadrom (the 'leaf traces') among the green cells of the cortex. As pointed out above, we must guard against a temptation to compare hadrom and leptom with xylem and phloem of vascular plants. Hadrom cells lack both the lignification and the characteristic pitting of tracheids; and leptom cells are not seive elements.

Lorch[138] noticed that in many pleurocarpous mosses the conducting strand was better developed in erect subaerial shoots than in prostrate creeping stems. He pointed out that dendroid mosses often had the hadrom cells in the central strand of the creeping stem collapsed, whilst these same cells were healthy in erect stems. We can now appreciate that many ectohydric mosses will have no call for functional water-conducting tissues in the lower parts of their stems and some apparent anomalies noted by Lorch are explained. The lower parts of ectohydric species are in fact quite often dead.

It may be noticed, furthermore, that genera such as *Rhacomitrium*, *Orthotrichum*, *Ulota* and *Cryphaea*, which lack a central strand, are also among the best examples of ectohydric mosses. Here, then, later work has cast a new light upon anatomical facts which had long been known. *Sphagnum* is interesting in this connection. Its water economy is essentially of the ectohydric type and the older parts of shoots are commonly dead. At the same time it has in its descending wick-like branches an efficient device for external capillary water conduction. As we might expect, the stem lacks a central strand, but shows an interesting tissue differentiation.

This chiefly concerns the superficial layers, one to three cells deep, which consist of wide, thin-walled cells, often with holes (pores) for direct entry of water. Immediately internal to this tissue lies the zone

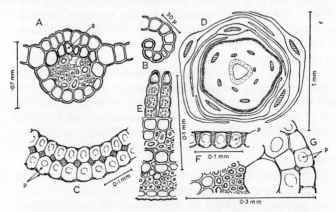

Fig. 18 Anatomy of mosses. A. *Bryum bimum*. T.S. midrib of leaf, showing extensive tissue differentiation. g. 'guide cells'. B. T.S. margin of same leaf. C. *Leucobryum glaucum*. T.S. leaf, showing layer of green cells between two layers of hyaline cells. D and E. *Polytrichum formosum*. D. T.S. aerial stem, with the sheathing bases of several leaves. Central clear area: hydroids (hadrom); stippled area external to it: leptom. There follow cortex, with some chlorophyll, and outermost sclerotic zone. Hatched areas are strands of hydroids which can be seen in leaf sheath midribs and as 'leaf traces' in stem. E. Part of T.S. leaf, near base of limb. Two relatively short lamellae are seen, and extensive tissue differentiation in midrib. F and G. *Sphagnum palustre*. F. T.S. part of leaf. G. T.S. sector of stem. p. 'pore' (which is a true hole in cell wall)

of small thick-walled cells (Fig. 18G). In species such as *Sphagnum rubellum* the walls of these cells are red with a closely held anthocyanin pigment. They are not lignified and are thus misleadingly described as 'woody cylinder'.

Less easy to understand fully, even in the light of modern experimental work, is the highly organized tissue differentiation in the transverse sections of some moss leaves. Among the best examples are species of *Mnium* and *Bryum* (Fig. 18A), in which the midrib of the leaf reveals four distinct kinds of cell: (1) upper and lower epidermis; (2) a group of relatively large, angular cells in the position occupied by xylem in the leaf of a vascular plant; (3) a compact group of minute, thin-walled cells reminding one of phloem; and (4) as a buttress underlying the latter, a group of small cells with very thick walls. At first sight there would seem to be some parallel here with the arrangement of tissues in the leaf midrib of a sclerophyllous vascular plant. Yet this is something of an illusion. For we have no assurance that water conduction is the special province of the second group above—the large, prominent cells which taxonomic botanists know as 'guide cells'. The precise role of the small, thin-walled group is unknown, and they display none of the special features of phloem. Finally, the apparently sclerotic tissue is neither lignified nor need it be principally for support.

So far as thickenings of the cell wall are concerned among bryophytes, Lorch implied repeatedly that their chief function was water storage. This would be true alike of the many instances of heavy wall thickenings in leaf cells and the thick-walled cells of fibre-like form ('stereids') which are mentioned above. Of the former the longitudinal walls in the base of the leaves of *Rhacomitrium* species provide a good example. The so-called trigones, which are intercellular thickenings found in the leaves of many liverworts, are in the same category. In some cases (cf. *Odontoschisma macounii*) these are as large as the associated cell cavities. Stereids may be seen in the leaves of such genera as *Bryum* and *Mnium* where the midrib is narrow; again in *Campylopus* and *Polytrichum* (Fig. 18E), where it is exceptionally broad.

The resistance of bryophytes to desiccation is a subject that is only imperfectly understood. It has long been known, for example, from the early investigations of such men as Irmscher[113] and Malta[147], that different species possess widely divergent powers of resistance. Thus, *Fontinalis squamosa* (an aquatic moss) is said to be unable to withstand a week of air-drying; whilst *Philonotis fontana* died only after fifteen to twenty weeks of this treatment; and the well-known xerophytic moss *Grimmia pulvinata* withstood sixty weeks in a desiccator at 20°C. More recent investigators have been

Mirimanoff-Olivet[155], Höfler[101], Ochi[167] and a number of others. Hosokawa and Kubota[107] tested many Japanese epiphytic species for ability to survive in different relative humidities. They found that at a relative humidity (R.H.) of 20% no species survived beyond a few days; and only two species could survive beyond two weeks at R.H. 30%.

It must be stressed that bryophytes differ fundamentally from vascular plants in their water relations. They are able to undergo severe drying out, only to recover immediately in the first shower of rain. This, which is an adaptation to intermittent (as opposed to high or low) water supply, is expressed by the term pollacauophyte. Accordingly, any xerophytic adaptations which have been attributed to mosses or liverworts (cf. Watson, W.[249]) will not operate in quite the same manner as they would in higher plants. Repeatedly it has been shown (cf. Clausen[49]) that it is the ability of a particular species to withstand drying out, rather than its ability to hold water as such, that affords a measure of its xerophytic adaptation. All such devices as the white (dead) hair points of the leaves in some mosses, or the in-curling thallus margins (protected by ventral scales) in some liverworts, must be interpreted with caution; although they may well serve to protect more vulnerable tissues from the effects of direct insolation. It is possible that thickened cell walls (discussed above) have a part to play in holding tenaciously that minimum quantity of water which is necessary for survival. Lorch believed so, but it is likely that their precise role is not yet fully understood.

On the question of resistance to heat as such Lange (1955) has shown a strong correlation between heat resistance and habitat. Thus, *Gymnomitrion obtusum* (moist mountain rocks) and *Plagiothecium curvifolium* (shaded woodland sites) were damaged by 70°C; whilst amongst species capable of surviving temperatures approaching 110°C were *Pleurochaete squarrosa*, *Tortula ruralis* and *Tortella nitida*, all of them inhabitants of rocks (or other surfaces) commonly exposed to intense insolation. Lange's experimental plants were thoroughly dried over phosphorus pentoxide, then exposed to the given temperatures for half-hour periods.

Some sections of bryophyte physiology remain little explored, among them many aspects of nutrition and metabolic activity. Here again, however, there is a link with fine anatomy, for the discernible contents of cells may provide valuable pointers. Starch and oil are both abundant and widespread, although starch storage organs in the sense that they occur in higher plants are rare among bryophytes. Much information on starch occurrence was put together long ago by Rancken[189]. Columella, seta and the delicate sheath (vaginula) about the base of the sporophyte may all at times contain quantities of starch. So, according to Lorch, may the thin-walled leptom cells in the central strand of most Polytrichaceae. It is of interest to note that whilst immature bulbils of *Pohlia* spp. (cf. Chapter 7) are rich in starch, the store appears to have been largely converted to oil by the time that the bulbils are ripe.

One to several large oil drops are often a feature of spores; but here too it has been noted that before the shedding of the capsule lid both oil and chlorophyll content of spores are much less marked than at a later stage, when the lid has been shed and the capsule is ripe. Earlier workers (cf. Lorch[138], Joensson and Olin[116]) detected a tendency for oily reserves in some bryophytes to decrease in February, only to mount again during the later spring months. Stored fatty material is said to account for some 18% of the dry weight of the moss *Rhodobryum roseum*. Besides spores and bulbils, another site where fatty (oil) droplets often abound is in the cells of the antheridial wall.

It seems clear then that the chief demonstrable carbohydrate (starch) and the most economic storage product (fatty oil) are the same in bryophytes as they are in most higher plants. In the comparatively large chloroplasts of such a species as *Funaria hygrometrica* the grains of transitory starch are easily seen (when the leaf is treated with tincture of iodine). As in higher plants, the grains of storage starch are larger and of quite a different shape. The oil droplets of bryophyte spores and bulbils find a parallel in the oily food reserves of many Angiosperm seeds.

The so-called oil bodies of liverworts are in an entirely different category. Their composition, not fatty oil at all, has been touched upon earlier (cf. Chapter 3), but rather little is known of their physiological significance. Clearly, the massive deposits which occur in certain cells of the thalloid liverwort *Lunularia* are not at all the same as the microscopic granules which by their diverse shapes and surface markings help the taxonomist to distinguish between closely related species in many genera of leafy liverworts. Schuster and Hattori[210], for example, have provided a comprehensive and fully illustrated treatment of these oil bodies, from the taxonomic standpoint, in the Lejeuneaceae, but they tell us nothing of their functional significance.

Finally, as regards the mineral nutrition of bryophytes, such studies as that of Tamm[226] on the moss *Hylocomium splendens* are among the most informative that we have. This author made extensive analyses, from which he found, among other things, that the percentage of nitrogen, phosphorus and potassium decreased with increasing age of the 'segment', whilst calcium tended to increase steadily. The experimental plant was convenient since its annual increments formed clear-cut 'segments' that enabled each to be subjected to separate analysis. Although the absolute quantities of mineral elements required by bryophytes are not great, Tamm was much concerned as to the source of these in a plant such as *Hylocomium splendens* which in later life has little or no direct living contact with the substratum. He pointed out that Romell[198] had been forced to the conclusion that the phosphorus supply to mosses from below was often inadequate and therefore some must come from elsewhere. The suggested source, which Tamm believes to be of great importance as a source of both phosphorus and potash for *Hylocomium splendens*, is the 'tree leachate', i.e. the washings from the leaves of overhanging branches of trees. Fallen leaf litter can also supply nutrients but may be detrimental owing to its smothering effects. Atmospheric dust washed down by rain is another source. Tamm remained puzzled, however, as to exactly how *Hylocomium splendens* obtained its nitrogen supply.

Richards[196], in an important review of recent work on bryophytes, alludes to further aspects of their physiology which have received attention. Some of these, such as growth studies, belong almost as much to ecology, and it is to this wide subject that we turn in the next chapter. Perhaps the foregoing pages will have served to emphasize the truth that the experimental morphologist, the anatomist and the physiologist are constantly making available data which can help the ecologist to interpret his findings. We must now consider just what these findings are.

10

Ecology

BRYOPHYTE ecology is the study of the part played by mosses and liverworts in various plant communities. It is concerned with the importance of particular species and with their relationship one to another. The subject has grown with increasing rapidity in recent years. Many nineteenth-century bryologists who knew well the habitats of the plants which they studied must indeed have been skilled in some facets of the subject. They would have known the habitat preferences of different species and the groups of species which it was usual to find growing together. Most often, however, they were not experimentalists, and it is the experimental side of bryophyte ecology which has extended so greatly during the past forty years or so.

The species list from a particular habitat may well form the starting point, and provided it be carefully compiled, and the habitat clearly defined, this list can be of value. Bryophyte lists in general works such as *The British Islands and their Vegetation*[227] have tended to come from diverse sources and to be uneven in quality. Those in this great classic of plant ecology came in part from W. Watson, himself a pioneer in this field, whose numerous papers on the bryophytes and lichens of various habitats[250-2] formed the foundation on which much subsequent work was to be built. Even this able bryologist did not always explain how far his lists rested on observations at single sites, how far on compilations from diverse sources. Nevertheless, these early papers are a mine of useful information and can still be consulted with profit.

The species list tells us at a glance the contrast between the component bryophytes of acid heath and those of chalk down, or again between the colonists of bare peat and the pioneers on maritime sand. From such lists we learn the value of 'indicator' species, such as *Ditrichum flexicaule* and *Encalypta streptocarpa*, which point at once to base-rich conditions; or the species of *Polytrichum* and *Rhacomitrium* which are almost without exception acid 'indicators'. Again, there are those species with habitat so circumscribed that their presence on a list can reveal the precise conditions prevailing. *Leskea polycarpa*, on tree roots liable to flood-water, is an example. Or the species individually may mean little, but taken together they may define a habitat with precision. Thus, the presence together of the liverworts *Nardia scalaris* and *Diplophyllum albicans*, and the mosses *Ditrichum heteromallum*, *Oligotrichum hercynicum*, *Pohlia elongata* and *Polytrichum urnigerum* will be highly suggestive of a fine-grained mountain detritus, moderately acid, on a fairly steep slope and at a not excessive altitude. A short list from a particular niche is often more informative than a longer, comprehensive one. Even so, at its best the species list is only a beginning.

A natural step forward is to include a consideration of succession. Ecology owes this term to the pioneer American ecologist F. E. Clements[50], and it alludes to the orderly sequence of change in vegetation as it proceeds towards what Clements called the natural 'climatic climax' where some kind of stability or equilibrium is reached. One of the first successional sequences (termed seres) in which the part played by bryophytes was clearly set forth was that on burnt heath (Fritsch and Salisbury[69]). Here these and subsequent observers have found that *Funaria hygrometrica* is among the first colonists, to be followed in sequence by *Ceratodon purpureus* and then *Polytrichum juniperinum* and *P. piliferum* in association with lichens of the genus *Cladonia*. The first two phases are passed through in perhaps a couple of seasons, but the third phase commonly lasts for many years. The phases are not always clear-cut, but the abundance of *Funaria* is demonstrably associated with the short period when the substratum shows a high pH and a high nutrient status (especially potash) following the fire.

Again, Richards[193] investigated bryophyte succession on sand dunes and concluded that at Blakeney mosses were prominent at early and late stages but were of less importance during the middle phase of succession. Thus, species such as *Bryum pendulum* and *Brachythecium albicans* can be early colonists in the lee of the main seaward dune ridge, whilst far back on the fully fixed dune pasture quite another group of species, including *Rhytidiadelphus triquetrus* and other large 'pleurocarps', will achieve prominence. Richards himself indicated some of the special adaptations possessed by the widespread dune moss *Tortula ruraliformis*, and Gimingham has since[81] described the special powers of *Bryum pendulum* and *Barbula fallax* to withstand burial by sand and to grow up through the layers deposited. Altogether more stable conditions prevail where the big pleurocarpous species achieve their maximum; so that here, as in all true successions, altered conditions dictate the changing flora.

Leach[131], studying non-calcareous screes, found bryophytes prominent in three distinct types of habitat, on the surfaces of rocks, in chinks between them, and thirdly as part of the invading 'heath' flora. Once more a succession may be detected as one passes from the second of these stages to the third. The liverwort *Diplophyllum albicans* Leach found to be the principal colonist of the chinks, whilst the later stages were marked by an increasingly varied bryophyte element. On the Cader Idris massif in North Wales, on acid granophyre block scree, I have found the small moss *Grimmia doniana* prominent on the surface of the blocks, *Rhacomitrium lanuginosum* the principal colonist in the deep clefts between blocks, and about a dozen species of bryophyte commonly contributing to the more stable vegetation that marked the ultimate phase in the succession. This included tall species of erect habit, like *Dicranum scoparium* and *Polytrichum alpinum*, species with rich and varied branch systems like *Hypnum cupressiforme* and *Rhytidiadelphus loreus*, and several robust leafy liverworts such as *Plagiochila spinulosa* and *Anastrepta orcadensis*.

Bryophyte ecology may be extended in a number of directions, and it will be our purpose now to examine some of these. Six topics will be discussed in turn, the first four with emphasis on the community (synecological), the last two with emphasis on individual species (autecological). Each has been the subject of at least some recent work. They are: (1) Attempts to recognize and define bryophyte communities; (2) recognition of different growth forms among bryophytes and attempts to use the system erected in subsequent experimental study; (3) use of quantitative methods in the description of bryophyte vegetation; (4) the time scale in succession; (5) a more refined study of the habitat, leading to a greater understanding of the precise ecological distribution of species, and (6) the detailed investigation (autecology) of a single species.

Clements put forward the notion of a plant community as a close-knit unit, with a life of its own which he likened to that of a living organism, divisible into phases of growth, maturity and senescence. There were those who asked to what extent bryophytes could form a community of this kind. Or was the bryophyte cover little more than the haphazard juxtaposition of species, often in keen competition but unworthy of the name of community at all? One or two examples may help to clarify the position. On old elders (*Sambucus nigra*) one may find a mossy covering containing perhaps the following seven species: *Orthotrichum affine*, *Zygodon viridissimus*, *Bryum capillare*, *Ceratodon purpureus*, *Brachythecium rutabulum*, *Hypnum cupressiforme* and *Cryphaea heteromalla*; and with them, close-pressed to the bark, may be the liverwort *Frullania dilatata*. On a number of grounds this may be said to constitute a bryophyte community. On old elders, over a wide geographical area, this group of species, or one very like it, will be found; the species will be competing with, and reacting upon, one another, but mutual benefit is also possible through conservation of rainwater, amelioration of microclimate and so on; the different species, each with its own morphology and growth rate, are in a sense parts of one whole; and finally, at a certain point in the life of the elder tree the community had a beginning, it achieves maturity when all species are present and fully grown, and in the foreseeable future, some time after the death of the tree, the life of the community will end.

Some case can be made then for the recognition of bryophyte communities. Difficulties arise, however, when one considers the manner in which a particular bryophyte cover may change over the years. Thus, if one is following the course of events on a fallen bough, through the long period of decortication and decay, until a patch of raw humus is all that remains of the branch that once supported a group of epiphytic mosses, then surely one must speak of a succession of communities. There will be, first of all, the community of epiphytes borne by the living branch. This will be followed by a group characteristic of dead wood in a very different microclimate (almost that of the forest floor). In due course the decorticated log will present a surface of soft, well-decayed wood for colonization by such species as the liverwort *Nowellia curvifolia*, the loss of bark surely heralding the onset of a new community again. When at last the branch crumbles to raw humus a final community ensues, with *Campylopus piriformis* probably the chief member. Doignon[63] has reported that this sequence of events may take some twenty-five to thirty years in the forest of Fontainebleau. In northern Scandinavia, according to Barkman[10], it may well take several hundred.

Herzog[99], in an enumeration of the bryophyte communities of the Black Forest mountainous region, has designated them by reference to their most characteristic species. He sometimes finds a single species that defines the community, as with *Polytrichum strictum* (*P. alpestre*) which indicates drying out of the upper layers of bogs. It is described as pushing up through the *Sphagnum* cushions and in its establishment it is associated with certain lichens (*Cladonia, Cetraria*), but with few bryophytes. We can see it doing the same thing in some mountainous parts of Britain. More frequently Herzog's communities are marked by at least two characteristic species, as in the *Philonotis seriata-Bryum schleicheri latifolium* community, where associated species are numerous and together give a clear picture of the prevailing conditions. The list includes *Pohlia albicans* var. *glacialis, Bryum duvalii* (*B. weigelii*), *Calliergon* (*Acrocladium*) *stramineum, Dicranella squarrosa* and several large species of *Scapania*. It resembles what I have myself seen in some of the high flushes in the Cairngorms.

Herzog's system is a good one, provided it is not used too rigidly. The French bryophyte ecologists Doignon[60] and Gaume[79] have given clear pictures of events in Fontainebleau and in Brittany respectively without recourse to any rigid system of community designation. Some followers of the Zürich-Montpelier school of phytosociology, however, have been inclined to insist on a strictly hierarchical system of nomenclature. In his early article in the *Manual of Bryology*, Gams[75] laid the foundation for this as applied to bryophytes and in a subsequent contribution[76] he reviewed the position twenty years later. Barkman[10] has recently made very extensive use of such a system in his account of cryptogamic epiphytes in the Netherlands. This system makes for precise description, and an immense body of fact has been amassed by means of it. A study of the second part of Barkman's monumental *Phytosociology and ecology of Cryptogamic epiphytes* will show the kind of result achieved. The system can, however, be a little too rigid.

Another method of attack was that adopted by Gimingham and Robertson[83] in their *Preliminary investigations on the structure of bryophyte communities*. Here the emphasis was on growth form, regarding which the authors built on the earlier foundation laid by Meusel[154] and others before him. Their first working scheme of growth forms in bryophytes was subsequently modified (Gimingham and Birse[82]), although its main essentials were retained. Five categories of growth form are recognized—cushions, turfs, canopy formers, mats and wefts (Fig. 19). Most of these are further subdivided, but the canopy formers (with such mosses as *Thamnium*, *Climacium* (Fig. 19J) and *Mnium undulatum*) compose a single group on their own. A size difference separates large cushions (such as *Leucobryum*) from small cushions (such as species of *Grimmia* (Fig. 19A) and *Ulota*). Again, tall, short and open turfs are recognized, with *Polytrichum commune*, *Bryum argenteum* (Fig. 19B) and *Polytrichum aloides* respectively as an example of each. *Breutelia chrysocoma* exemplifies a special kind of tall turf with abundant rhizoidal development on the stems; *Campylium stellatum* and *Sphagnum* (Fig. 19D) are cited as illustrations of 'tall turfs with divergent branches of limited growth'. Mats prove difficult and in the four subdivisions are included such diverse forms as *Eurhynchium striatum* (rough mat), *Frullania tamarisci* (smooth mat), *Eurhynchium praelongum* (thread-like) and finally members of both Marchantiales and Metzgeriales under the heading of thalloid mats. Wefts are more straightforward, and although in the original version the authors separated 'spreading branched' from 'pinnately branched' wefts they have later replaced this subdivision by one based on frequency of rhizoids. Hence *Hylocomium splendens* (Fig. 19H) is a relatively rhizoid-free weft, *Thuidium tamariscinum* one with frequent tufts of rhizoids.

The need for some workable system of growth-form classification had indeed long been felt and on page 128 of his classic *Bryo-*

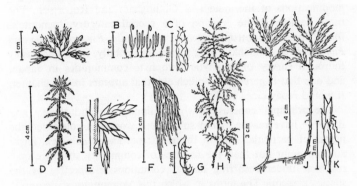

Fig. 19 Some growth forms of mosses. A. *Grimmia pulvinata*; small cushion. B–C. *Bryum argenteum*; short turf. D–E. *Sphagnum recurvum*; special kind of tall turf, with fascicled branches of limited growth. F–G. *Hypnum cupressiforme* var. *filiforme*; mat. H. *Hylocomium splendens*; weft. J–K. *Climacium dendroides*; canopy former. C, E, G and K represent small portions enlarged to show detail.

géographie de la Suisse Amann[4] set forth in outline a system put forward two years earlier by Herzog. This made the primary division into solitary (*Rhodobryum roseum*) and colonial forms, and the latter group was further subdivided into eight categories, several of which were the same as those of Gimingham and Robertson. The system was less comprehensive than theirs and is now of mainly historical interest.

Gimingham and Robertson explained that a single species could at different times fall into different growth-form categories. Even so, the decision as to where to place a particular example will not always be easy to make. Fortunately, Gimingham and his co-workers have followed the original paper with numerous studies in which the scheme has been employed in the ecological analysis of bryophyte vegetation. The system has also been used by various workers in other countries, notably in America and Japan.

Iwatsuki[114] is a good example of a Japanese ecologist who has used this tool, but in doing so he has made a number of slight modifications of the system of Gimingham and Robertson. The most notable is the erection of a special category, 'pendulous forms' for such subtropical genera as *Barbella*, *Pseudobarbella* and *Floribundaria*. Iwatsuki's long paper, incidentally, is an immensely thorough survey of epiphytic bryophyte communities in Japan, and one that is germane to much else that appears in this chapter. It would repay close study.

The principal conclusion which Gimingham and Birse[82] and Birse[13,14] have reached from subsequent work has concerned the fitness of particular growth forms for particular habitats. These authors point out that 'the features of community structure may reappear under recurring habitat conditions irrespective of the species present'. The terms in which this 'community structure' is expressed are the growth forms. Two illustrations may be given. In the first of these reference is made[82] to the zonation of bryophytes in a deep ravine. From running water one passes successively through four zones: *Eurhynchium riparioides*, *Cratoneuron filicinum*, *Conocephalum conicum* and finally *Thamnium alopecurum*. The presence of these last two is used to point the habitat requirements of 'thalloid mats' and canopy formers'—i.e. conditions of increasingly high relative humidity. The question that remains unanswered is why other species, exhibiting these same growth forms, do not appear in the positions indicated.

A second illustration comes from sand dunes where ground water supply differs markedly in different parts of the dune system[14]. Here the presence of *Tortula ruraliformis* on dry areas is taken as warranting the conclusion that the growth form 'tall turf with erect branches' is characteristic of such sites. *Tortula ruraliformis* has several special features which fit it for life on partially fixed dunes, features to which Richards[193] referred when he tried to explain its supremacy in this specialized habitat. If it is correctly styled a 'tall turf with erect branches' it is still a very different plant in every way from another that is so classified, namely *Polytrichum commune*; and one doubts whether the possession of this particular growth form by *Tortula ruraliformis* is in itself of the first importance.

The growth-form system of Gimingham and his co-workers is an important recent contribution to bryophyte ecology; but it is essential that we should understand both its advantages and its limitations if it is to take its proper place in the future development of the subject. To some minds any such system has one great inherent weakness, in that it rests on externally visible structural pattern. In a word, it is morphological rather than biological. In order to appreciate this, one has only to note that two such very different genera biologically as *Sphagnum* and *Polytrichum* are placed together under the single head of 'turfs'. On the other hand, *Eurhynchium striatum* (rough mat) and *Hylocomium splendens* (weft) may well have very similar biological economies. Recognition of different growth forms may be of less real significance than Buch's separation of bryophytes into endohydric, ectohydric and mixohydric groups, to which reference was made in the last chapter.

The bryological literature of Great Britain is rich in accounts of the mosses and liverworts which characterize most of the important habitats to be found in our land. Many such contributions have appeared in the *Transactions of the British Bryological Society*. Of these the accounts by Paton[174-5] of the Wealden sandstone in Kent and Sussex have emphasized a particular habitat, where an exceptional flora for south-eastern England is linked inseparably with the outcrops of a certain kind of rock. In many more cases, however, valuable ecological information is enshrined in fully annotated county bryophyte floras (Rose[149], Jones[118], Proctor[185], Swinscow[224], Paton[176]). Many areas of Britain have been covered in this way, and between them these accounts enable a clear picture to be formed of the ecological amplitude of various species. Moreover, an increasing number of general ecological accounts can be found which give due weight to the bryophyte element. To mention but three, one may cite the series of papers by various authors on the vegetation of the Cairngorms (cf. Watt and Jones[253], Burges[33]), the recent full account of the Silver Flowe in Galloway, by Ratcliffe and Walker[190] and Rose's comprehensive treatment of the bryophyte element[200] in British Lowland bogs. Plenty of information is to hand; what is less common is to find this in an exact, quantitative form.

By way of illustration, we may take the study of chalk grassland. Here, Hope-Simpson[104] was able to lay the foundation of our knowledge of the bryophytes by preparing lists of species occurring respectively in mature ('closed') grassland and in seral stages. He also named the eight species which were the most important and constant in chalk grassland as a whole. Letters 'a' (abundant), 'f' (frequent), 'o' (occasional) and 'r' (rare) were appended to each of the species in the main lists. We know that some fifty sites were sampled, but we do not know the size of these; nor do we know the criteria used in determining which letter was to be appended to each species. A recent study (Watson[246]) of a more limited area of chalk grassland has depended upon the use of definite and readily repeatable sampling methods. It confirmed Hope-Simpson in placing *Pseudoscleropodium purum* as the most generally abundant moss of chalk grassland, but figures demonstrated that it was approximately three times as plentiful as its nearest rival species.

Perring[180, 181] has used a clear-cut sampling method in his detailed investigation of chosen aspects of chalk grassland ecology. These concern the sensitivity of particular species to different slopes and aspects and to differing climatic regimes. By such methods bryophyte ecology is taken a step forward. Numerical evidence is adduced to show, for example, that in north Dorset the mosses *Weissia microstoma*, *Eurhynchium swartzii*, *Neckera complanata* and *Fissidens cristatus* are confined to the steeper slopes of aspects between south-east and west. Strictly comparable sites near Rouen, near Cambridge, in Dorset and in Yorkshire were compared, and it was found that *Hylocomium splendens* and *Rhytidiadelphus squarrosus* were among the species which were absent from the

Rouen site and even in Dorset were confined to slopes between north and east.

Just as it is helpful to have quantitative studies of ecological distribution, so one would like to know the exact time required for the completion of particular successions. Reference has already been made to the work of Doignon, in France, on the succession of bryophytes on rotting logs. The same author tells us[61] that when fire destroys old heather moor (*Callunetum*) with its attendant bryophyte cover of such species as *Pleurozium schreberi*, *Hypnum cupressiforme* var. *ericetorum* and *Dicranum scoparium*, it may well be thirty years before this type of bryophyte flora is restored, so gradual are the various stages of regeneration.

Barkman[10] gives a vivid account of succession on a living tree, which was studied by Doignon in the forest of Fontainebleau. Lichens colonized first and twenty-five years of the tree's life had passed before the liverwort *Frullania dilatata* arrived, closely followed by species of *Orthotrichum*, *Ulota* and other genera. When the tree was some thirty-five years old there came mosses of the genera *Anomodon* and *Neckera*, and the liverwort *Porella platyphylla*. Finally, after forty years, *Leucodon sciuroides* and *Zygodon viridissimus* colonized the mature tree.

The study by Bliss and Linn[16] of 'old-field' succession in the Piedmont of North Carolina is an example of a rapidly changing environment supporting a succession of bryophyte communities. The expression 'old field' is in general use in America for fields that have been allowed to revert as cultivation marched westward, and every ecologist familiar with the American scene knows the meaning of 'old-field pine' (*Pinus* spp.) and 'old-field cedar' (*Juniperus* spp.) as the names for important conifers which step in after the land has been abandoned. Bliss and Linn found the richest bryophyte community that of the first full season after cultivation had ceased, some seventeen species succeeding the pioneer, *Sphaerocarpos texanus*. At the four- to seven-year period pine became conspicuous, and from eight to fifteen years saw the transition to full dominance of pine. Fifteen years after abandonment the number of species of bryophytes had dropped to five. Thereafter changes were rather gradual over many years. Observations suggested that after a lapse of some period well over 120 years pine would be superseded by deciduous trees; and these would entail an entirely new range of bryophyte communities.

Apart from successional sequences of this kind, there are instances where a favoured site has been known to support the same group of bryophytes, or maybe a particular species of moss or liverwort, for 80 to 100 years, or as far back as records go. Yet we may know little of its fluctuations in abundance over the years, of how often and how successfully it reproduces, vegetatively or by spores, or what is the exact age of the larger cushions or tufts. Some moss shoots reveal their age readily and reference has been made (Chapter 9) to the 'segments' of *Hylocomium splendens*, each representing one annual increment. Again, one sometimes finds the moss *Breutelia chrysocoma* with several successive seasons' capsules at different levels on the old stems, and it may be easy then to assess the age of the tuft. Most often the life of an individual plant or colony is short and lack of change in the site as a whole is something of an illusion.

I am familiar with an outcrop of greenstone on the Isle of May, Firth of Forth, where the cushions of the rather rare moss *Grimmia stirtoni* have been known for at least eighty years. By marking a permanent quadrat on the outcrop one was able to see that the life of a particular cushion may be short indeed, and within seventeen months there had been big changes in the distribution of the colonies of this moss[247]. The chart quadrat method (where each plant is drawn or symbolized) may be usefully employed in work of this kind.

The relationship between bryophyte pioneers and subsequent vascular plant colonists can also be studied by this method. Although many people think of bryophytes as early colonists (often following algae and simple lichens) which give place to vascular plants later, this is only partially true. On many sites, on boulders, roofs, cliff-faces and some kinds of unstable scree, only casual vascular plants may succeed in gaining a footing; and the bryophyte cover may be a kind of environmentally conditioned 'micro-climax' of its own. A certain stage in development is reached. Then some natural phenomenon, such as frost action or snow melt, results in the removal not only of the little community but of part of the substratum too. A fresh surface is laid bare, and the whole process starts all over again. In mountain cliff habitats some such cycle of events must be very common. One would like to know more of the exact time-sequences involved.

Life on the trunks and branches of trees will provide a good example of modern emphasis upon the more refined study of the habitat; for here mosses and liverworts are an important component of the flora, and Barkman[10] has given a penetrating analysis of the whole environment. He points out that different sides of a tree-trunk may present very different microclimates; and this for three main reasons. These concern (1) the aspect of trunk (or branch) in relation to the daily march of the sun, (2) aspect in relation to the direction of the prevailing wind, and (3) the inclination of the trunk from the vertical position. Thus, deep in a ravine, a tree may have the same epiphytic vegetation all round the trunk. Barkman cites Kraemer[126] as having been the first to point out the advantages of a leaning trunk. The value of the off-vertical habitat so created seems to lie mainly in its power to catch and retain atmospheric precipitation. Once a bryophyte cover has been formed, this enhances the effect and cuts off the under surface of the leaning trunk from any appreciable water supply.

No full grasp of the varied habitat conditions offered to epiphytes is possible without some appreciation of the differing potentialities of the bark of different species of tree. Apart from properties associated with bark character (rough or smooth, hard or soft, and so forth) two chemical factors, as Barkman shows, are very important. These concern nutrient supply and acidity. The rich epiphytic flora associated with elder (*Sambucus nigra*) is partly related to the high nutrient status of its bark. This has 8–12% ash content in the dry bark and in reaction it approaches neutral (pH range 5·5 to 7·0). By contrast, species of *Picea* (spruce), *Abies* (silver fir) and *Pinus* (pine) tend all to be low in nutrient status and markedly acid in reaction. On these conifers the bryophytes are few. Trace elements such as boron, cobalt and molybdenum, which in recent decades have proved important in crop nutrition, are not known to exert any influence in bark ecology.

There is a much richer epiphytic flora in woods in western Britain, as compared with the south-east. The cushions of *Leucobryum glaucum*, ordinarily a ground species, may be seen ascending the trunks of trees; the communities are richer in species, and the total bryophyte cover on favourably placed trees is much more extensive. Barkman[10] refers to *Dicranum fuscescens*, which, he says, will grow on tree bark in wet forests, on rotten logs in moist ones and on the ground (raw humus) in dry ones. Thus, he considers that it behaves as a microclimatic indicator. In the Rothiemurchus pine forest of Inverness-shire it can be seen in all these three situations, in different parts of the forest.

Maritime conditions, as might be expected, affect the epiphytic flora of trees that grow in coastal dunes or other situations within reach of salt spray. According to Barkman, the high humidity induced by such a situation (coupled with the high water capacity of elder bark) enables mosses like *Acrocladium cuspidatum* and *Leptodictyum riparium* to appear on sand dune elders; for these are not common epiphytes.

Richards[194] referred to certain mosses that were able to grow in the splash zone and could thus be classed as genuine halophytes. The outstanding example is *Grimmia maritima*, its blackish-green cushions being a feature of so many maritime rocks in western Britain. *Ulota phyllantha* at times grows with it, not far above high-water mark. Shacklette[212] studied a halophytic community of bryophytes on Latouche Island, Alaska, and found *Tortella flavovirens*, *Pottia heimii*, *Camptothecium sericeum*, *Hypnum cupressiforme* and *Grimmia maritima* all to be salt-tolerant. The special conditions of this type of habitat, and the way in which they operate on the few bryophytes capable of colonizing such ground, await further investigation.

Shacklette in the same paper discussed the peculiar group of bryophytes able to grow in areas that are exceptionally rich in copper, a subject to which Persson[183] had earlier given attention. Persson gave figures showing the copper content of the mosses themselves (in parts per million) and the pH of the substratum. He did this for species of 'copper moss' belonging to the three genera *Mielichhoferia*, *Dryptodon* and *Merceya*, and although the copper content varied it tended always to be high and could be as high as 675 parts per million. On Latouche Island Shacklette detected several distinct cuprophile communities, and in one case the liverwort *Gymnocolea acutiloba* grew practically pure over a wide area, forming a kind of 'liverwort peat' several inches thick. He also named a group of bryophytes tolerant of high gypsum content, and another of species which grew on substrata rich in sulphide of iron. These, however, are not peculiar to such habitats in the way that the copper mosses are, for they are seen to include species well known in quite different habitats in Britain. Among the gypsum-tolerant are *Dicranella cerviculata* and *Cephalozia bicuspidata*, widespread on peat in this country, and among the sulphide-tolerant are *Rhacomitrium fasciculare*, *Oligotrichum hercynicum* and *Nardia scalaris*, which abound on acid rock and scree habitats generally.

The investigations of Grønlie[89] have shown that a special vegetation develops on ground exceptionally enriched by the droppings of sea birds (guano). He worked on the famous bird cliffs of Røst, in the Lofoten Islands of northern Norway, and (following earlier workers) he termed the plants tolerant of such conditions ornithocoprophilous. Grønlie listed over forty bryophytes on the bird cliffs of Røst, and named a number of them as strongly ornithocoprophilous. Among these were *Ceratodon purpureus*, *Eurhynchium praelongum* and *Mnium hornum*, all of which are also prominent on the Isle of May (Watson,[243]), where great colonies of sea birds nest. We do not know what makes a species tolerant of heavy bird manuring. The three named above are certainly all plants of wide ecological amplitude in Britain as a whole.

Richards[194] emphasized the difficulty of isolating the effects of a particular ecological factor, for it is clear that to alter one factor of the environment is to disturb others at the same time. Some progress can be made, however, when modern methods are brought to bear on the study of a chosen factor. This is what Clausen[49] did in her admirable study *Hepatics and humidity*. She worked on an area in East Jutland sufficiently limited to enable her to make a thorough study of the hepatic flora and to correlate distribution with accurate measurements of relative humidity. Her paper should be consulted for the details of the methods used. So refined were they that they allowed extreme localization of readings; and Clausen quotes an example from the steep bank of a lane where *Nardia scalaris* enjoyed a relative humidity of 85% whilst only 5 cm away, on a slight prominence, *Frullania tamarisci* was subject to 55%. Such results throw a new light on the micro-environments in which mosses and hepatics are growing.

For our final topic we turn briefly to those studies which emphasize individual species as such, the autecological approach. By this kind of specialization (as noted in Chapter 9) Tamm[226] was able to advance our knowledge of the moss *Hylocomium splendens*, its habitat selection, growth rhythm and nutrition. Intensive studies on this scale are not numerous. The work of Tallis[225] on *Rhacomitrium lanuginosum*, however, has thrown light on the ecology of an outstandingly interesting and important moss. For here is a plant which occurs in such abundance on certain kinds of mountain-top detritus that it has given the name '*Rhacomitrium* heath' to the vegetation which it dominates. Yet one sees it also (as already mentioned) as the pioneer on some kinds of block scree; or again as a late-comer in the succession on certain types of old bog. I have seen it in such a role on the Isle of Barra, Outer Hebrides, where it formed mound-like cushions half a metre across. It abounds on many types of substratum in base-poor mountain country; it is surprisingly widespread on limestone in northern England, and, most remarkable of all, occurs in a few places on the chalk of the South Downs, growing in the turf quite close to known calcicole species. Such a moss presented a challenge indeed, so that the comprehensive study by Tallis was all the more welcome. Moreover, as Tallis himself points out, *Rhacomitrium lanuginosum* is a moss of world-wide distribution.

In his first paper Tallis assessed the role of *Rhacomitrium lanuginosum* in different communities. In his second paper he considered growth form, growth rate, manner of reproduction and several features of the plant's physiology. Among other things, he showed that the white hair-points on the leaves were longest in dry, sunny weather in the summer; also, it was between May and

August that maximum growth occurred and lateral branches were best developed. The annual growth increment was always small, however, varying from 5 to 15 mm in length. This slow growth rate, and the fact that some, at least, of its physiological activities are at their optimum within a narrow temperature range (13–15°C), suggested that this moss might succumb easily in the face of competition. Tallis was inclined to attribute part of its success in many barren and inhospitable sites to a capacity (for which he finds some evidence) to render soluble some normally insoluble components of the substratum.

Within the limits of a single chapter it has been possible to touch upon but a few selected topics of bryophyte ecology. Anything approaching a descriptive account of the ecology of British bryophytes was out of the question. By referring to some of the sources mentioned, and by experience gained from field observations, the interested student will build up his own picture of the ecological ranges of different species. So, too, will he gradually acquire a knowledge of important bryophyte communities to be found in the various plant associations.

Bryophyte ecology is no self-contained subject. It may often serve to illuminate the path of workers in other fields. H. Watson[248] has indicated how useful some of the larger bryophytes can be as guides to the practical forester concerning the condition and character of the land. I have been informed of a case in which the remains of a lost village in a forest in Austria (Hörmann, *in litt.*) were traced through the presence of the moss *Mnium undulatum*; for it had selected the locally enriched ground where the former village had existed before being burnt down during the Thirty Years' War. Again, as Persson[183] has said, the 'copper mosses', to which reference was made earlier in this chapter, could be of interest to ore prospectors.

On an altogether wider front, an account of the bryophytes is an integral part of the description of any piece of vegetation where they occur. Nowhere is this more conspicuously so than in bog ecology, where *Sphagnum* is of outstanding importance. Nine or ten species of this genus between them, and each in its own specialized niche, play such essential parts in bog succession that no ecologist can afford to ignore them*. Rose[200], Ratcliffe and Walker[190], and others, in dealing with different kinds of bog, and Tansley in his general account[227], have given them their due. To attempt to do so now would entail another full chapter.

---

*Two modern keys to British species of *Sphagnum* exist: Proctor M. C. F. (1955). Trans. Brit. bryol. Soc. 2, 552. Duncan, U.K. (1962) Trans. Bot. Soc. Edinb. 39, 290.

11

Geographical distribution; geological history; cytogenetics and speciation

IN THIS chapter we are concerned with three big, interrelated topics. The distribution of families, genera and species in the world today must to some extent reflect the history of these groups. Palaeobotany can tell us more of this. Moreover, the cytogeneticist can provide us with an additional point of view; and, more important, he can tell us something of how new species arise and how existing ones are interrelated. A survey of bryophytes would be very incomplete without some enquiry into these three branches of knowledge.

The most direct challenge made to the botanist by any group of plants is that of their diversity. He must describe them and learn to recognize the different 'kinds'. To this end the taxonomist erects his species, grouping together in a single genus those which show certain salient features in common. In the early days bryophyte genera tended to be few. All manner of mosses, many of which are now known to be quite unrelated one to another, were crowded into the genus *Bryum*; so too with the comprehensive genus *Hypnum*, and with *Jungermannia* among leafy liverworts. Later taxonomists saw that such a practice could be misleading, as well as resulting in impossibly large and unwieldy genera. So men like Fleischer, early in this century, drew up generic limits on a much narrower basis, and the number of genera increased enormously. There are those who are concerned[221] lest the concept of genus should perhaps have become too narrow in recent years, at least in the hands of some bryological taxonomists. Much the same fate has overtaken the concept of family, and we saw some evidence of this in our introductory chapter.

These facts are mentioned here because valuable conclusions regarding geographical distribution can be drawn only if the preliminary taxonomic work is securely founded. After that we must have the enumeration and description of countless forms of moss and liverwort, followed by a general exploration of all the great regions of the world, before the material is assembled on which the student of geographical distribution can begin to work. It is a testimony to the industry of the early bryologists that something like this state of affairs had been attained by 1926, when Herzog[98] compiled his monumental work *Geographie der Moose*.

In this book the great German bryologist not only brought together a vast wealth of information, but outlined the principal patterns of geographical distribution to be seen among bryophytes and went on to draw conclusions from them.

If the world distribution of taxa is to have a meaning we must be clear on two points. The first is that a given taxon is most unlikely to have arisen independently in two or more places. The second is that so-called long-range dispersal by spores is not a normal event. There are those who have supposed that because mosses and liverworts reproduce by light air-borne spores the distribution of any species will rapidly become very wide indeed, with the result that the distribution patterns revealed by species (or other taxa) will be of little interest. Herzog convincingly upheld the opposite view, namely that long-range 'jumps' are almost as unusual among bryophytes as they are among flowering plants. Fulford[72], who more recently has been much interested in the same problem, supports him; and she points out that the chance of spores being carried great distances by air currents and then being deposited in a viable state is in most instances remote, for the good reason that whilst they are indeed light and easily air-borne they quickly lose viability when allowed to dry. Fulford cites particularly the green spores of the leafy liverwort family Lejeuneaceae which have ordinarily begun to germinate before leaving the capsule. In any event, the facts of known distributions of bryophyte taxa are very far from revealing a uniform, nearly world-wide distribution for all species, or even genera.

It is true that certain species, among them many of the commonest British mosses, have a cosmopolitan distribution. These are the least interesting, and I suspect that many are in the nature of 'international weed species', which owe part at least of their world-wide distribution to the activities of man. In this group, among mosses, are *Ceratodon purpureus*, *Tortula muralis*, *Funaria hygrometrica*, *Bryum capillare* and *Bryum argenteum*. Also of nearly world-wide distribution, however, are some species which do not grow on waste ground, wall tops and other man-made sites—plants like *Gymnostomum calcareum* and *Drepanocladus uncinatus*. These and others are assigned by Gaume[78] to the class of cosmopolitan species in his analysis of the bryophyte flora of Brittany. *Hypnum cupressiforme*, often regarded as the most 'variable' of British mosses, is said to be cosmopolitan, but Herzog pointed out that if we were to accord specific rank to three of the most marked 'varieties', *lacunosum*, *resupinatum* and *ericetorum*, we should see, in the first a Mediterranean, in the other two plants an Atlantic, type of distribution.

Much, therefore, will depend on our concept of species. So too with genera, and for this reason Herzog was careful to focus attention on well-established genera about which no great controversy was raging. Even so, many big genera, such as *Bryum* with some 800 species, *Grimmia* and *Barbula* each with over 200 species, and, among liverworts, vast genera like *Plagiochila* (1,200 species), *Frullania* (500) and *Lophocolea* (350), have world-wide distributions and consequently hold rather little interest for us. Sometimes, however, a large genus may be split into sections each of which has a specialized distribution. Herzog showed this to be true of *Philonitis*, which had distinctive palaeotropical, austral-antarctic, Patagonian, tropical east Asiatic and north temperate sections, in addition to the section *Eu-Philonotis* which was north temperate in the main, but with outlying species in the Andes and the Himalayas.

This brings us to the two kinds of distribution pattern, which have most greatly interested plant geographers. These are, first, disruptive patterns of distribution and, second, endemism (the restriction of a taxon to a given region or country). Herzog's account is full of examples of disruptive generic distributions and we can mention only a few of the most striking. Thus, there is the curious large-spored genus *Gigaspermum* with representatives in Australia, South Africa and Morocco; and *Echinodium* which is found in the Azores and Madeira, reappearing only in many parts of Australasia. We find the British genus *Myurium*, with *M. hebridarum* showing an Atlantic type of distribution, but with other species appearing in Indo-Malaya and extending to Samoa, a very remarkable disjunction. At the specific level *Anoectangium compactum* is notably disjunct, for besides having a wide range in the north temperate it reappears in the Andes and New Zealand.

A number of prevailing patterns of disjunction may be recognized. Thus there are species (e.g. *Plagiothecium undulatum*) found in Atlantic Europe and reappearing in western North America; others that are well-known Mediterranean plants (e.g. *Pottia starkeana*) which reappear in the similar climatic conditions of California. Schuster[209] has drawn attention to a group of Western European species which reappear in North America principally or exclusively in the southern Appalachians. More remarkable perhaps is the New Zealand-Patagonia disjunction; or the so-called bi-polar type of distribution, where a genus is known from both arctic and antarctic regions. In such instances the Andes may have furnished a migration pathway. In order to explain other patterns of disruptive distribution we may have to look to a different conformation of the great land masses of the world from that which prevails today.

Fulford[72] has returned to this subject afresh in her study of South American liverwort genera. She notes that *Blepharostoma* and *Anastrepta*, among others, show a bipolar type of disjunct distribution. Several genera, all of which display 'many primitive or simplified characters', have a widely disjunct distribution in the southern hemisphere as a whole. Among these are *Calobryum*, type genus of the isolated group Calobryales, and *Zoopsis*, which Goebel noted long ago as displaying a strangely alga-like vegetative habit. Specific disruptive patterns are well shown within the genus *Acromastigum*, where one species is found in Chile, Australia (including Tasmania), New Zealand and the Auckland Islands, whilst another occurs in Malaya with an outlying station in Sikkim.

Certain genera show an Australasian-South American disjunction which is exactly paralleled by particular sections of each of the Gymnosperm genera *Podocarpus* and *Araucaria*. Most interesting of all, perhaps, are *Herpocladium* and *Lepidolaena* which seem to be basically antarctic genera of leafy liverworts; yet each has an outlying representative far away in the Sikkim Himalaya. The explanation, Fulford considers, can lie only in the fragmentation of a flora that, rather more than a hundred million years ago, must have existed relatively uniformly over much of the southern hemisphere; a southern hemisphere, moreover, of very different configuration from the one that we know today.

Endemics, it seems, are of two principal kinds. When a plant inhabits a single country it is either because that plant is very ancient, having vanished from its former stations elsewhere, or because it is so recently evolved that it has lacked the time to achieve a wider distribution. Fulford would add a third kind, the intensely specialized, whether they be young or old historically. Fourteen genera of tropical leafy liverworts found in South America are regarded by her as either old or intensely specialized endemics. Most have a single known species (monotypic genera) and it seems likely that they represent structural patterns that were once more widespread. The erection of a third category is perhaps undesirable, for it blurs the sharp line which would otherwise separate the very old from the very new; and some degree of specialization, moreover, is surely to be expected in all endemics. Certainly, among other great groups of organisms, one can find endemics that are truly ancient, and are as specialized in structure as they are limited in geographical distribution. One thinks of the hoatzin among birds, the tuatara among reptiles and plants like *Welwitschia* and *Metasequoia* among Gymnosperms. Bryophytes that are comparably arresting are not easy to find, but Herzog mentions one that stands alone taxonomically and is confined to Tasmania and New Zealand. This is *Pleurophascum grandiglobum*, with its inordinately large capsule borne up on a long seta but nevertheless completely cleistocarpous. Here indeed is a truly ancient kind of moss, with no known close relatives. Herzog described it as a 'living fossil'.

At the other end of the scale are endemics of recent origin, and in these we can sometimes see a vicarious pair of species which have been separated long enough to evolve into recognizably distinct taxa. Herzog quotes *Coscinodon cribrosus* in Europe, with its counterpart *C. trinervis* in the Andes. Fulford mentions some of the very numerous 'micro' genera of Lejeuneaceae, in South America. She contends that some of these are relatively recently evolved, and limited in distribution for that reason, although she believes Lejeuneaceae as a whole to have originated at a very early period. It has been remarked that bryophytes tend to be much poorer than higher plants in examples of 'neo-endemics', because they are geared to a slow rate of evolution and have been evolving for a very long time indeed. How true this is we shall see by turning to the evidence of the fossil record. Before doing so, however, we must remind ourselves that not all really ancient forms are reduced to endemic status. On the contrary, certain mosses which we have reason to regard as old, for example the genera *Buxbaumia* and *Diphyscium*, have a very wide, though somewhat scattered, distribution. Indeed most kinds of disruptive distribution pattern imply considerable antiquity, for only by looking for historical causes can we find an explanation for them. Some disruptive distributions, it is true, have been brought about by events as recent as the Pleistocene Glaciation and we have among bryophytes certain examples of 'Tertiary relicts', survivals of a richer flora that prevailed in a warmer epoch that preceded the Ice Age. The secret of many disjuncts, however, and among them those that interested Fulford the most, lies much further back in time. A certain kind of endemism and some kinds of disruptive distribution are the two most eloquent testimonies that we have, of a phytogeographical nature, concerning the ancient origin of particular forms. More than that the fossil record must supply.

It has sometimes been said that bryophytes are so poorly represented in the fossil record that a discussion of these fossils can contribute nothing of value to the general question of moss and liverwort evolution. There might have been some truth in this view forty years ago; but it is far from true today, and is likely to become less so as time goes on.

We are fortunate in having a useful summary of the fossil

contribution in a paper entitled the *Geological Annals of the Bryophyta*, by Savicz-Ljubitzkaja and Abramov[204]. These authors point out that, although the artificial 'form genus' *Muscites* was founded by Brongniart as long ago as 1828, the nineteenth-century work as a whole was characterized by an absence of microscopic detail. So far as pre-Tertiary fossils showing any wealth of fine structure are concerned we must look to the work of palaeobotanists in the twentieth century and more particularly to the period from 1925 onwards when many of the newer palaeobotanical techniques had become available. The authors give figures for the total numbers of known pre-Tertiary fossil bryophytes (in 1959). These are, for the Mesozoic, fourteen liverworts and three mosses; for the Palaeozoic, seven liverworts and nine mosses (almost all these mosses coming from a single recent contribution to which reference will be made later). For the Tertiary period, by contrast, the figures given are thirty-five liverworts and 134 mosses. The latter tend on the whole to be exceedingly like known living forms, and it is to the pre-Tertiary fraction, at first glance so pitifully small, that we must turn our attention.

Few in number though they may be as yet, we shall see that the early fossil bryophytes can provide us with some kind of answer to two very important questions. The first is the question as to how far back in time the two great groups, mosses and liverworts were differentiated. The second is something that all keen students of living bryophytes will wish to ask the palaeobotanist: did there exist, some hundreds of millions of years ago, in Palaeozoic or early Mesozoic time, bryophytes that were quite unlike any present-day living form?

The year 1925 was something of a landmark, for it saw the publication of the first account of Carboniferous liverworts in sufficient detail to leave no doubt as to what kind of plants they were. On this occasion[238], and again in 1928[239], Walton made it clear that there existed in the Coal Measures certain liverworts which bore a fairly close resemblance to some modern Metzgeriales. Thus, *Hepaticites willsi* was thalloid after the manner of *Riccardia*; but *Hepaticites kidstoni* was a clearly leafy form, though not perhaps in the sense that Jungermanniales (Acrogynae) are so today.

F

At first glance the fossil in Walton's plate looks very like one of these, but in addition to two ranks of major leaf-like organs it appears to have borne other, much smaller appendages and Walton looked towards *Treubia* (in the Metzgeriales) as the nearest living ally of this ancient fossil. It is tantalizing that this early leafy liverwort stands alone and that hitherto the rocks have revealed no allied form that could throw further light upon it.

Also standing very much alone, and also leafy, is the remarkable Mesozoic plant *Naiadita*. This had long been a well-known feature of certain layers in the Rhaetic when Harris[93], after a very detailed examination involving several new techniques, revealed its true nature. Then, for the first time, it was shown to display, time and again amid its exceedingly abundant remains, a whole series of bryophyte features. Axis and foliar structures, rhizoids, gemmae, archegonia, even a sporophyte of general form strongly reminiscent of the living genus *Corsinia*, all these were laid bare in remarkable clarity of detail. Only one organ was lacking; nowhere could be found unequivocal remains of antheridia. The work on this fossil stands alone among fossil bryophyte investigations, not only for its great wealth of detail, but also for the strange, baffling picture of a liverwort that emerges.

In a point-by-point summary Harris was able to bring a considerable weight of evidence to suggest that its nearest living ally may have been *Riella* (Sphaerocarpales). The form of the leaves (though not their arrangement, which was moss-like), the rhizoids, the relation of archegonia to perianth and the structure of the large spores, all these were brought reasonably into line with *Riella*, but in the sum of all its characters *Naiadita* may fairly be claimed as unique. Given such detailed knowledge of a single fossil bryophyte, bryologists would easily be tempted to do too much with it, were it not for the cautious note on which Harris ends his paper. He insists that we beware of the temptation to regard *Naiadita* as the common ancestor of diverse living forms just because it combines features found in certain genera belonging to different families today. The history of individual organs, he reminds us, is still dark.

At different times within recent years some light has been shed on the remote past of the liverwort group Marchantiales. Lundblad[142] and Townrow[231] have described fossils from the Rhaetic-Liassic of Scania and the Middle Triassic of Natal respectively. (See also Harris[93a].) The upshot is that we know that there existed in Mesozoic times members of the order Marchantiales that must have been extraordinarily like some living genera of that order. In *Ricciopsis scanica* Lundblad describes and figures a fossil liverwort which bears a convincing resemblance to some modern species of the genus *Riccia*. In *Hepaticites cyathodoides* Townrow sees resemblances to *Cyathodium* in habit, and in the structure of midrib, rhizoids and ventral scales, but the 'pores' that occurred on the upper surface of the thallus were unlike those of the modern genus. Here then are two Mesozoic fossils (and there are others) which can be brought fairly closely into line with modern genera of the Marchantiales. What of the other major living groups?

Although a fine series of Jungermanniales from Tertiary times has been found preserved in the Baltic amber we have no exact knowledge of this group from earlier geological periods. Again, early fossils which can be brought into line with Calobryales or Anthocerotales are quite unknown; nor is there any form which can throw light on the early history of the Andreaeidae, with their curious type of capsule structure and dehiscence. Indeed, on the whole subject of the early history of sporophytes the fossil record is almost completely silent; and no hint has been forthcoming as to how the peculiar liverwort pattern of structure, with elaters playing a decisive role, or that characteristic adornment of the moss capsule, the peristome, came into being. We are left to conjecture.

The past of several groups, then, remains shrouded in darkness. Not so the Sphagnidae (or bog mosses) and the Bryidae (true mosses), on which in recent years the researches of Neuburg[160-2] in the U.S.S.R. have shed a flood of light. This palaeobotanist has not only given the first really informative account of true mosses from rocks of Palaeozoic age, but, thanks to the good stage of preservation of the fossils and the use of modern peel-transfer techniques, she has been able to describe the available fragments in extraordinary detail. She has not hesitated to depart from palaeobotanical convention and erect a number of new genera, based on fairly narrowly defined criteria and often named after the locality of origin. In the genus *Intia*, for example, Neuburg has four species which bear some remarkable resemblances to the modern genera *Mnium* and *Bryum*. The leaf dimensions and shape, cell structure and thickened, toothed leaf border (Fig. 20A)—all are there. The only cause for regret is that we have been left no trace of any reproductive organs.

The fossil mosses described by Neuburg, however, do more than tell us that there lived in Permian times several types of undoubted

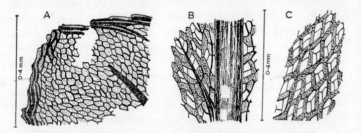

Fig. 20 Fossil mosses from the Permian. A. *Intia variabilis*. Part of leaf, showing border, nerve and leaf cell structure. B and C. *Protosphagnum nervatum*. Portions of leaf, B, near nerve, C. away from nerve, to show 'pattern' of cell arrangement. (All adapted from Neuburg, and all the same scale.)

Bryidae very like those that are alive today. They shed a most interesting light on the early history of *Sphagnum*. Arnold[8,9] had already shown that *Sphagnum* went back at least to the Cretaceous; and Reissinger[192] obtained both leaves and spores of this genus from the Jurassic (Lias) near Nuremberg, in Bavaria. Neuburg[162] has taken the story a stage further back, but what she lays bare is not *Sphagnum* as we know it today. She has erected the group Protosphagnales, to contain (at present) the three fossil genera, *Jungagia*, *Vorcutannularia* and *Protosphagnum*.

In varying degree the fossil leaves included here resemble the leaves of modern *Sphagnum* in being composed of two kinds of cell. Yet these have not differentiated so far as in the modern bog-mosses where the large, dead water-holding cells (with their specialized thickenings and 'pores') are strikingly different from the narrow, living green cells. These fossils seem rather to have resembled the condition seen in very young *Sphagnum* leaves today. Convincingly like *Sphagnum* though they may be with their 'elementary triads' of cells, these early leaves depart from it in one very important respect—they have a midrib and sometimes traces of lateral veins as well (Fig. 20B,C).

How far the leaf cell pattern is exactly that of *Sphagnum*, and how far it is something superficially very like it but fundamentally rather different, may be a matter for debate. In any event it is clear that there lived during Permian times in what is now Angaraland (U.S.S.R.) mosses with a leaf structure unmatched in any genus alive today. If these, and liverworts like *Naiadita*, are not 'common ancestors' of major living groups which have since diverged, they are at least ancient forms of bryophyte whose precise structural pattern has become extinct in just as real a sense as have the body forms of dinosaurs and pterodactyls.

Muscites guescelini, described by Townrow[231] from the Triassic of Natal, may well be an example comparable with the above, for it could not be brought perfectly into line with any known living moss. It lacked the arresting features of most of Neuburg's fossil genera, however, and in many respects came close to modern mosses of the family Leucodontaceae. Again one regrets the absence of reproductive organs.

Few though the early fossils may be, they can furnish some answer to the two questions posed on page 161. These fossils indeed imply that the principal groups of both hepatics and mosses must have been differentiated by the end of the Palaeozoic. Savicz-Ljubitzkaja and Abramov[204] would not be surprised to find forms clearly attributable to moss or liverwort as far back as the Silurian. Their origins appear buried in the very remote past, with the liverworts, on balance, probably the older of the two. Our second question has been answered for us by *Naiadita* and *Protosphagnum*. There did exist in Palaeozoic and Mesozoic times bryophytes unlike those we know today; so that, on the evidence available, they are difficult to place in any known major group.

Of the considerable wealth of more recent fossils we have said nothing. This is because they have little to contribute to the particular questions that we have raised. In quite another field, that of Quarternary botany, or the study of changing floras during and since the Ice Age, bryophytes are becoming increasingly important. Associations of arctic species found in Interglacial or very early post-glacial deposits in parts of southern England testify to the conditions then prevailing. The recent literature has many scattered records of 'sub-fossil' finds of this type; finds of striking arctic species such as *Paludella squarrosa* and *Meesia triquetra* (cf. Godwin and Richards[84], Landwehr[128]) in regions whence they have long since gone, to mention but two from a host of records which are helping to clarify the history of our flora. This is the meeting ground of palaeobotanist and plant geographer.

Turning now to our third topic, we find that Allen[1,2] twice reviewed the extensive literature on the genetics of bryophytes. More recently Lewis[135] has contributed a general paper of great intrinsic interest. On the purely cytological side, following the earlier survey by Sinoir[215], comprehensive catalogues of the known chromosome numbers of mosses and liverworts have been provided by Wylie[263] and Berrie[12] respectively. Lowry[140-1], Bryan[27-8] and Steere[222] have been among those in the United States who have made important contributions in recent years. So too with Vaarama[232] in Finland; Yano[264] and Tatuno[229,230] in Japan; Mahabele[146] and others in India. There has been no lack of recent literature and the output is expanding.

Bryophytes have a distinguished place in the history of genetics. Not only did the liverwort *Sphaerocarpos* provide a classical instance of sex chromosomes, but mosses of the genera *Funaria*, *Physcomitrium* and *Bryum* furnished Wettstein[254-5] with the material for experiments of fundamental importance, more than thirty years ago. He made successful inter-generic crosses; he showed that the resulting plants leaned more towards the female than the male parent in their characters and was thus led to postulate a maternal cytoplasmic influence. He repeatedly raised new leafy gametophytes from protonema that had grown as a regenerant from fragmented seta; and he was hence able to obtain plants carrying high multiples of the original chromosome number and to demonstrate the effects of such high polyploidy on the structure of the moss, both gross and minute. Finally, Wettstein and Straub[257] succeeded in synthesizing a 'new species' of the genus *Bryum*, *B. corrensii*, with twice the normal number of chromosomes, and fully monoecious, unlike *Bryum caespiticium* whence it came.

Most often the investigator who requires information about the chromosome complement of a moss seeks the spore mother cells at the stage when they are entering the 'reduction division' (meiosis) to form four spores (the tetrad). The capsules are fully swollen but are usually still bright green. Steere[222] tells us that the time when the annulus (or ring between capsule body and lid) begins to be pigmented is a good guide to the presence of suitable stages within. A Carnoy type, acetic acid-absolute alcohol fixative is commonly employed and this is followed at once by a specific stain for chromosomes such as synthetic orcein in 45% acetic acid. Appropriate amounts of heat and pressure are applied and a 'squash' preparation of meiotic figures results. Early in meiosis the chromosomes come together in pairs, forming the 'bivalents', and a count of these gives the cytologist the haploid chromosome number of the plant in question.

If we turn to the long list of chromosome numbers for liverworts published in Berrie's useful paper, we may have to agree with his opening comment, that 'the Hepaticae are well-known cytologically', but we shall also notice that the whole picture is complicated by the presence, in the majority, of additional chromosomes of various kinds. Sometimes these are sex chromosomes; at other times they are odd-sized chromosomes with peculiar staining properties, the full significance of which is as yet imperfectly known. Although of great interest to the cytologist, these need not concern us here. Suffice it to note the prevailing chromosome numbers and the incidence of polyploidy.

In some 75% of all liverwort species investigated so far the basic haploid number is 9. A long series of species of *Riccardia* (and the non-green *Cryptothallus*) are exceptional in having 10 as their basic number, whereas 5 comes up for the known Anthocerotales and 4 for the unique and recently discovered *Takakia lepidozioides*. Elsewhere, in a short paper which he admits is a 'phylogenetic speculation', Berrie[11] indicates how these figures might be used to support the view that *Anthoceros* and its allies were primitive, for an evolutionary sequence in chromosome numbers of $5 \to 10 \to 9$ has a certain air of probability. The basic number, 8, runs through most Ricciaceae and Sphaerocarpaceae, occurring again without exception in all those species of *Madotheca* which have been investigated by Tatuno or Segawa in Japan.

Polyploidy among the hepatics does not seem to be very common, but it is interesting to see that the abundant and widespread leafy liverwort *Cephalozia bicuspidata* has been found with both 18 and 36 as the haploid chromosome number. The thalloid liverwort *Dumortiera hirsuta*, of the Marchantiaceae, has been found with 9, 18 and 27. Altogether, the liverworts form a strong contrast with the mosses cytologically, in the comparative uniformity of their basic number, in the abundance and variety of their 'accessory chromosomes' and in the comparative scarcity of polyploid series.

Perhaps on the whole the mosses are less well known. For although Wylie[263] has provided a useful and comprehensive summary there are only 364 species listed in her table. If this table is complete it means that less than one-fortieth of all moss species that have been described are cytologically known; not a very large fraction, and plenty of room for future work. There is a range of basic haploid numbers, with 11, 12 and 13 predominating in Dicranales, Pottiales and Grimmiales and occurring widely elsewhere as well. Thus the basic number in *Pohlia* is 11, as it seems also to be in *Hedwigia*, *Thamnium*, *Anomodon* and *Entodon*. In *Bryum* it is 10, in *Mnium*, *Orthotrichum* and *Bartramia* 6, in *Polytrichum* 7 and in *Sphagnum* 21 $(19 + 2)$. In the face of such diversity it is difficult to read much meaning into the basic chromosome numbers of mosses and the situation is complicated by several additional features.

First, there are species such as *Fissidens taxifolius* and *Weissia controversa*, for which conflicting numbers have been returned by different observers. Then there is the baffling occurrence of astonishingly high numbers in genera that are structurally akin to others that display the normal basic number for the order. Most notable in both these respects is the familiar wall moss *Tortula muralis*, for which Wylie lists no fewer than six different chromosome counts, in English, Irish and Californian material (mostly determined by Steere[222], or by Vaarama[232]). All ranged from 40 upwards and the highest was 66, and this in the Pottiales where normal basic numbers run from 11 to 15.

Polyploid series are not only commoner in mosses than in liverworts. They have also proved of great interest on account of the changes in gametophyte structure which are sometimes associated with an additional chromosome complement. One such effect is the attainment of monoecism by the polyploid members of a genus that is ordinarily composed of dioecious species. This is well seen in *Mnium*, as Lewis[135] demonstrates, in which *M. orthorhynchum*, *M. affine* and *M. punctatum* all have ordinary haploid gametophytes and are dioecious, whilst *M. marginatum*, *M. medium* and *M. pseudopunctatum* all have double the normal complement and are monoecious.

In experimentally produced polyploids in the moss *Physocomitrium pyriforme* Wettstein[256] found that the addition of each successive complement of chromosomes was marked by a significant increase in the volume of the leaf cells. Thus the mean volume of leaf cells in 2n leafy shoots was twice that of leaf cells in ordinary haploid gametophytes. In 4n gametophytes (octoploid plants) it was almost eight times as big. Such big increases can have serious consequences, for the chloroplast complement of the cells often fails to go up at the same rate and the osmotic pressure of the cells in high polyploids may also be low. It is thus interesting to note that in naturally occurring polyploids such as those cited above in *Mnium*, there seems to be no correlation whatever between cell size and polyploidy. Each of the polyploid species mentioned in fact has leaf cells of a size very similar to those of its closest ordinary haploid relative (cf. Lewis[135]).

Work on flowering plants has suggested that the incidence of polyploidy is increased in high latitudes. Steere[222] investigated this point with reference to mosses from arctic Alaska. Fifty-five species, from thirty-five genera and eighteen families, were examined, and it was found that no clear increase in polyploidy in high latitudes could be demonstrated for mosses. A point raised incidentally by

Steere was the high frequency of minute bivalent chromosomes. A similar situation exists in *Sphagnum*, but a study of the drawings made by Bryan[27] in her paper on this genus shows the two so-called 'm' chromosomes (×1450) as minute dots. Their presence could surely have been overlooked on occasion; and it is probably safest to say that the extent of their occurrence in mosses as a whole is as yet imperfectly known. Sex chromosomes and chromosomes with exceptional staining properties have been rather widely acclaimed by some of the Japanese workers (cf. Yano[264-5]), but, as Wylie points out, one needs to know more about these before a clear picture can be formed.

Cytogenetics impinges most directly on the kind of problem posed at the beginning of this chapter when it is used as a tool in the study of some critical species or group. An admirable example is the work of Anderson and Bryan[6] on *Fissidens cristatus* and the closely related *F. adianthoides*. In Britain we know these two as mosses which appear somewhat alike but frequent rather different habitat ranges and can be distinguished by a number of small differences. The above authors, using material from Nova Scotia, not only demonstrated haploid chromosome numbers of 12 (+ 1) for *Fissidens cristatus* and 24 for *F. adianthoides* but adduced further cytological evidence for believing the two species to be less closely related than had been hitherto supposed. The cytological study was accompanied by a biometric analysis of leaf cell dimensions and a summary of all characters that could be used to separate the two species.

Many bryologists, embarking nowadays on the study of a critical group, begin with experimental cultivation. Lodge[136] has cultivated critical species of *Drepanocladus* (*D. exannulatus* and *D. fluitans*) with illuminating results. Extensive changes in habit could be environmentally induced, whilst certain cell characters, especially those of the 'alar' cells in the leaf base, remained highly constant. Wherever such cultivation work is combined with critical cytological study the way is made clear for a deeper understanding of species and their interrelationships. An earlier and specially notable example of a rather different kind was the monumental work of Burgeff[32] on *Marchantia*, for it combined long-term genetic experiment with large-scale taxonomic research. Moreover, it led its author to important phylogenetic conclusions.

Space has allowed us to touch only briefly upon three big topics. Selection of material has not been easy, for the literature is extensive. It is probably true to say that, so far as bryophytes are concerned, all these fields of study, the phytogeographical, the palaeobotanical and the cytogenetic—are as yet only in their infancy. Using very different methods and exploring what seem at first sight to be very diverse fields of knowledge, they combine to throw light on the real nature of the living mosses and liverworts which we meet with in the field and study in the laboratory or the herbarium. The herbarium worker most of all must guard against undue isolation.

12

Conclusion

THE gross morphology of a bryophyte is chiefly of interest in an evolutionary context. If there is a sense of evolutionary sequence then all information regarding the comparative structure of different forms is of interest in that it reveals the place of each in the sequence. In the absence of any clear-cut or widely accepted picture of evolution in the group as a whole the morphology of individual genera loses much of its significance. In some degree that is the position reached today.

We are in possession of the basic facts regarding the morphology of numerous genera, among them types that may be considered crucial in the understanding of all the chief orders, of both mosses and liverworts, and some attention has been directed to them in the early chapters of this book. Here and there, in recent years, a plant has been uncovered which transgresses the limits of the orders hitherto known. One thinks of *Monocarpus* and *Takakia*. It is not possible to look upon such facts without wishing to take them a step further and fit them into some acceptable picture of the evolution of bryophytes as a whole.

When, however, we seek enlightenment from contemporary or recent assessments of bryophyte interrelationships, we must surely turn away in disappointment. For mosses there have been no recent assessments comparable with that of Fulford[71] for hepatics. The latter author is fair to every point of view; she states impartially the case of those who hold the homologous theory, and again of those who hold the antithetic theory, of evolution in Hepaticae. She mentions some unusual viewpoints, such as that of Kashyap. Yet nowhere does she point the direction in which she herself believes the truth to lie. The student is left to grope amid theories utterly conflicting and mutually irreconcilable. Should he go on to consult Smith[218] or Parihar[173] he will be taken no further towards a solution. Conflicting standpoints are again presented; and no decisive judgment is offered.

Yet, if we are to understand and appreciate the morphology of *Anthoceros*, or *Sphagnum*, or *Sphaerocarpos*—or any other of the long line of examples that have been passed in review in the foregoing pages—we must have some idea of the stage that it represents in the evolution of the Bryophyta. It seems strange to us today that men like Cavers were so certain about these matters. They put forward a logical argument and were themselves utterly convinced by it. The interpolation of a new generation—the sporophyte— seen at its inception in *Riccia*, and mounting to a climax of near-independence in *Anthoceros*, this was the pillar on which much of the argument rested. Knock away this pillar, as did Wettstein, R.[258], Evans and others, and postulate instead two similar, radially symmetrical, green generations in the life of the primitive bryophyte, and the whole argument falls to pieces. Once this second viewpoint (the homologous theory) is adopted, a great part of what Cavers[43] wrote in 'The Interrelationships of the Bryophyta' is stripped of all meaning. Can it be that morphologists, spurred on by the possession of a definite viewpoint, have not always been sufficiently clear as to the true nature of evidence?

There have been sporadic revivals of interest in the interpretative morphology of bryophytes within recent years. Conspicuous in this field has been Mehra[151], who has put forward a carefully reasoned argument to account for the origin of the complex, chambered thallus of the higher Marchantiales from such Metzgeriales as *Petalophyllum*. Both idea and argument are ingenious, but not all will be convinced. Again, Christensen[47] and Haskell[94] are among those whose views will startle some morphologists, for they trace the ancestry of bryophytes direct from the simplest known vascular plants—i.e. the Psilophytales in the Pteridophyta. Most botanists still think of the earliest bryophytes as having come from pigmented thallophytes—probably from some form of green alga now extinct. Just how far back such an origin must have been is indicated by the fossil bryophyte record, as we saw in Chapter 11.

Anybody reading the varied viewpoints currently put forward on bryophyte interrelationships would be justified in referring to this as a time of speculation, where interpretative morphology is concerned. Perhaps the only honest conclusion to draw is that we do not know how these organisms are interrelated. Nor do we know from what earlier organisms the remote ancestors of present-day mosses and liverworts came. We do not know, because there is insufficient reliable evidence to hand.

Faced with the present position, we can only hope that the gradually advancing fronts of knowledge, morphological, cyto-genetical, palaeobotanical and the rest, will provide us in time with sufficient new information to enable us to see more clearly how the different orders are interrelated. Then perhaps we shall be able to take a step further and learn something of how they evolved. Among the lines of evidence least open to criticism is surely that coming from vestigial structures. For example, the existence in the capsule of *Sphagnum* of non-functional stomata proclaims for that capsule an earlier existence as a photosynthetic organ of greater importance than the one we see today. The apparently functionless underleaves near the apex of the shoots in certain species of the family *Lophoziaceae* can hardly be other than a survival from a past in which these plants had a ventral rank of fully developed leaves. This kind of evidence has been largely used by advocates of the homologous theory. This theory calls for reduction on a very large scale, in the sporophyte especially, and *Riccia* is often cited as the end product of the process. In the absence of any known sporophyte in bryophytes with even a trace of appendages, however, it is not easy to be convinced by an argument which postulates two originally similar generations. It seems possible that some future botanists, whilst admitting widespread reduction, may prefer to return to Bower and Cavers for a consistent and logical picture of past events.

Fossil evidence is perhaps the most incontestable of all. We must await the uncovering of more early fossils before coming to any sure conclusion. Meantime the contemporary botanist is wise to withhold judgment.

If it is true that many problems of interpretative morphology must remain at present unsettled, it is equally true (and reassuring) that work goes on apace on the lives of bryophytes, on their morphogenesis, physiology and ecology. We have seen that strides have been made in these fields of study over the past thirty years or so; and this is but the beginning.

Bryophytes are unlikely to achieve great economic importance and hence to attract the limelight which that entails. It is nevertheless true that recent decades have seen a resurgence of interest in the group, an interest which is probably fully justified by what we have been able to see of their significance in ecology alone. Present-day accounts of vegetation tend to look incomplete if the bryophyte element is not included; and every year the weight of published information about the ecological status of important species becomes greater. Detailed autecological studies have taken our knowledge of certain species a step further still.

The taxonomic edifice is in differing degree necessary for all workers within the group. One needs to know with what species one is working. This is not always easy to ascertain, for, as at all times, there is no finality as regards specific definitions or limits; witness some of the recent revisions of groups of British mosses by Crundwell[53-4]. We have seen how cytotaxonomic work can help towards a better understanding of the species. At the same time one of the greatest needs of the present day is the revision of large genera which include numerous tropical representatives that have possibly never been submitted to critical reassessment since the date of their original description. A considerable body of work of this kind is being undertaken, most of it of necessity on limited regions. To cite only a few examples, we have the work of Fulford[70] on *Bazzania* in Central and South America; of Schuster[208] on Lophoziaceae—and other groups since; of Jones[120] on African hepatics (papers I to XV); of Clark and others on *Frullania*—in a long series of papers in *The Bryologist*. Japanese workers have been exceedingly active in this direction, and one may note, among others, the work of Noguchi[164] on Leucodontineae and Neckerineae, of Ochi[168] on Bryaceae. These last, and other admirably illustrated treatments, have appeared in the *Journal of the Hattori Botanical Laboratory*.

Every year sees the publication of descriptions of a number of new species, and we are driven to conclude that many parts of the world remain quite imperfectly explored bryologically. The handling of moss collections from remarkably diverse countries has been the special interest of Bartram (some forty papers, 1945–60), although bryologists from all over the world have of course played their part in this exploratory work. Often it must be hard to know whether a species is indeed new, so scattered is existing literature. There is a great need for improved co-ordination and the position has been well stated by Verdoorn[234] in his challenging article *The future of exotic cryptogamic botany*.

In Britain, alike among professional and amateur bryologists, there has been a long tradition of interest in geographical distribution of species. This, to be of value, presupposes species that are securely founded. For more than fifty years the area basis has been the vice-county, but currently certain species are being investigated on the much more thorough basis of the 10 km square as a unit of area. Rather remarkable has been the finding of over a dozen mosses and several hepatics new to Britain since 1945. Some, such as *Trochobryum carniolicum* (cf. Warburg[241]), have been finds of exceptional interest. The most recent* has been the finding of *Platygyrium repens* in Berkshire (Perry and Warburg[182]), where the facts suggest that it has been present for some time, but overlooked. This is hardly surprising since it is superficially very like some states of *Hypnum cupressiforme*. A range extension of *Platygyrium* to Britain is something that might indeed have been looked for long ago. More baffling in many ways is the 'sudden appearance' of the Californian moss *Tortula stanfordensis* in Cornwall (cf. Whitehouse[259]). Since its discovery in 1958 it has spread over a considerable area of cliff-top soil on the Lizard point. A recent addition to the British liverwort flora also comes from Cornwall. This is the discovery by Paton[176] of *Southbya tophacea* on a disturbed part of the sand dunes at Perranporth. There might have been some rash enough to suggest, twenty years ago, that the distribution of bryophytes in Britain was fully 'worked out'. The challenging discoveries of the past fifteen years have given the lie to any such notion.

* See also Trans. Brit. bryol. Soc. 4, pt. 3, 1963, where this and three further novelties are noted.

One final word to the beginner. In this book I have not hesitated to give extensive references to the literature, in the hope that the student will be led thereby to explore in depth, utilizing original sources. Yet the beginner must not expect any easy or rapid conquest of a difficult subject and he will surely be wise to proceed by way of general textbooks such as those of Smith and Parihar, through review articles, to the original papers; just as he may wish to begin with a simplified flora[244] and graduate to the handbooks of Dixon[58] and Macvicar[144]. At first he may be inclined to despair of ever learning to recognize even quite common species. For there is a double difficulty; the 'form circle' of individual species is often surprisingly wide whilst at the same time the boundary between two species can sometimes be fine indeed. It is well to remember that the exceptional eye, combined with taxonomic flair, is given only to the few. Far more than this can be bryologists; and there is much for them to explore. Richards[196] has looked back, down the 'vista' of the last half-century, and has traced many paths of progress. The young bryologist is privileged to look forward, down the long vista that lies ahead. Without doubt, new and exciting discoveries await him.

Bibliographical references

1   Allen, C. E. (1935). Bot. Rev. **1**, 269
2   Allen, C. E. (1945). Bot. Rev. **11**, 260
3   Allsopp, A. and Mitra, G. C. (1958). Ann. Bot. N.S., **22**, 95
4   Amann, J. (1928). *Bryogéographie de la Suisse*. Zürich
5   Andersen, E. M. (1929). Bot. Gaz. **88**, 150
6   Anderson, L. E. and Bryan, V. S. (1956). Rev. bryol. lichen. **25**, 254
7   Arnell, S. (1956). *Illustrated moss flora of Fennoscandia*. 1. Hepaticae.
    Lund
8   Arnold, C. A. (1932). Pap. Mich. Acad. Sci. Arts and Lett. **15**, 51
9   Arnold, C. A. (1947). *An introduction to palaeobotany*. New York
10 Barkman, J. J. (1958). *Phytosociology and ecology of cryptogamic
    epiphytes*. Assen
11 Berrie, G. K. (1958). Trans. Brit. bryol. Soc. **3**, 427
12 Berrie, G. K. (1960). Trans. Brit. bryol. Soc. **3**, 688
13 Birse, E. M. (1957). J. Ecol. **45**, 721
14 Birse, E. M. (1958). J. Ecol. **46**, 9
15 Black, C. (1913). Ann. Bot. **27**, 511
16 Bliss, L. C. and Linn, R. M. (1955). Bryologist, **58**, 120
17 Bopp, M. (1954). Z. Bot. **42**, 331
18 Bopp, M. (1959). Rev. bryol. lichen. **28**, 319
19 Bopp, M. (1961). Biol. Rev. **36**, 237
20 Bopp, M. and Stehle, E. (1957). Z. Bot. **45**, 161
21 Bowen, E. J. (1931). Ann. Bot. **45**, 175
22 Bowen, E. J. (1933). Ann. Bot. **47**, 401 et seq.
23 Bower, F. O. (1908). *The origin of a land flora*. London
24 Brodie, H. J. (1951). Canad. J. Bot. **19**, 224
25 Brotherus, V. F. (1924). Musci. Spezieller Teil. In Engler and Prantl,
    Die natürlichen Pflanzenfamilien, Bd. 10 and 11. Leipzig
26 Bryan, G. S. (1927). Bot. Gaz. **84**, 89
27 Bryan, V. S. (1955). Bryologist, **58**, 16
28 Bryan, V. S. (1956). Bryologist, **59**, 118
29 Bryan, V. S. (1956). Amer. J. Bot. **43**, 460
30 Buch, H. (1911). *Über die Brutorgane der Lebermoose*. Helsingfors
31 Buch, H. (1947). Soc. Sci. Fenn. Comm. Biol. **9**, 1
32 Burgeff, H. (1943). *Genetische Studien an Marchantia*. Jena.
33 Burges, A. (1951). J. Ecol. **39**, 271
34 Campbell, D. H. (1898). Bot. Gaz. **25**, 272
35 Campbell, D. H. (1918). *The structure and development of mosses
    and ferns*. 3rd ed. London. 708 pp.

36 Campbell, D. H. (1924). Ann. Bot. **38**, 473
37 Campbell, D. H. (1936). Bot. Rev. **2**, 53
38 Carr, D. J. (1956). Australian J. Bot. **4**, 175
39 Cavers, F. (1903). Ann. Bot. **17**, 270
40 Cavers, F. (1903). New Phytol. **2**, 121
41 Cavers, F. (1904). Rev. bryol. **31**, 69
42 Cavers, F. (1904). Ann. Bot. **18**, 87
43 Cavers, F. (1911). *Interrelationships of the Bryophyta*. New Phytol. Repr. no. 4. Cambridge. 203 pp.
44 Chalaud, G. (1931). Ann. bryol. **4**, 49
45 Chalaud, G. (1932). Germination des spores et phase protonémique. In Verdoorn, F., *Manual of bryology*, 89
46 Chalaud, G. (1937). Rev. gén. Bot. **49**, 111
47 Christensen, T. (1954). Bot. Tidsskr. **51**, 53
48 Clapp, G. L. (1912). Bot. Gaz. **54**, 177
49 Clausen, E. (1952). Dansk Bot. Arkiv. **15**, no. 1. 80 pp.
50 Clements, F. E. (1916). *Plant succession*. Washington
51 Coker, W. C. (1903). Bot. Gaz. **36**, 225
52 Correns, C. (1899). *Untersuchungen über die Vermehrung der Laubmoose durch Brutorgane und Stecklinge*. Jena
53 Crundwell, A. C. (1960). Trans. Brit. bryol. Soc. **3**, 706
54 Crundwell, A. C. (1962). Trans. Brit. bryol. Soc. **4**, 334
55 Davis, B. M. (1903). Ann. Bot. **17**, 477
56 de Bergevin, E. (1902). Rev. bryol. **29**, 115
57 Degenkolbe, W. (1937). Ann. bryol. **10**, 43
58 Dixon, H. N. (1924). *The student's handbook of British mosses*. 3rd ed. 581 pp.
59 Dixon, H. N. (1932). Classification of mosses. In Verdoorn, F., *Manual of bryology*, 397
60 Doignon, P. (1947). Bryophytes. In *Flore du Massif de Fontainebleau*. Paris
61 Doignon, P. (1949). Rev. bryol. lichen. **18**, 160
62 Doignon, P. (1950). Rev. bryol. lichen. **19**, 208
63 Doignon, P. (1952). Rev. bryol. lichen. **21**, 244
64 Evans, A. W. (1910). Ann. Bot. **24**, 271
65 Evans, A.W. (1912). Ann. Bot. **26**, 1
66 Evans, A. W. (1939). Bot. Rev. **5**, 49
67 Fleischer, M. (1902–22). *Die Musci der Flora von Buitenzorg*. Leiden
65 Fleischer, M. (1920). Hedwigia, **61**, 390
69 Fritsch, F. E. and Salisbury, E. J. (1915). New Phytol. **14**, 116
70 Fulford, M. (1946). Ann. Cryptog. Phytop. Waltham, Mass. **3**. 173 pp.
71 Fulford, M. (1948). Bot. Rev. **14**, 127
72 Fulford, M. (1951). Evolution, **5**, 243
73 Fulford, M. (1955). Rev. bryol. lichen. **24**, 41
74 Fulford, M. (1956). Phytomorphology, **6**, 199
75 Gams, H. (1932). Bryo-cenology. In Verdoorn, F., *Manual of bryology*, 323
76 Gams, H. (1953). Rev. bryol. lichen. **22**, 161
77 Gams, H. (1959). Rev. bryol. lichen. **28**, 326
78 Gaume, R. (1953). Rev. bryol. lichen. **22**, 141

79 Gaume, R. (1956). Rev. bryol. lichen. **25**, 1
80 Gemmell, A. R. (1950). New Phytol. **49**, 64
81 Gimingham, C. H. (1948). Trans. Brit, bryol. Soc. **1**, 70
82 Gimingham, C. H. and Birse, E. M. (1957). J. Ecol. **45**, 533
83 Gimingham, C. H. and Robertson, E. T. (1950). Trans. Brit. bryol. Soc. **1**, 330
84 Godwin, H. and Richards, P. W. (1946). Rev. bryol. lichen. **15**, 123
85 Goebel, K. (1905). *Organography of plants.* Vol. 2. Tranl. by Bayley-Balfour. Oxford. There is a later German edition (1930)
86 Gorton, B. S. and Eakin, R.E. (1957). Bot. Gaz. **119**, 31
87 Greene, S. W. and Greene, D. M. (1960). Trans. Brit. bryol. Soc. **3**, 715
88 Greig-Smith, P. (1958). Trans. Brit. bryol. Soc. **3**, 418
89 Grønlie, A. M. (1948). Nytt. Mag. Naturv. **86**, 117
90 Grout, A. J. (1928–40). *Moss flora of North America.* 3 vols. Newfane, Vermont and New York.
91 Guillamot, M. (1949). Bull. Soc. bot. Fr. **96**, 242
92 Györffy, I. (1940). Bull. Inst. roy. Hist. nat. Sofia, **13**, 207
93 Harris, T. M. (1938). *The British Rhaetic flora.* Brit. Museum
93a Harris, T. M. (1961). *The Yorkshire Jurassic Flora.* Vol. 1. (British Museum, Nat. Hist.) London, 212 pp.
94 Haskell, G. (1949). Bryologist, **52**, 49
95 Hattori, S. and Mizutani, M. (1958). J. Hattori bot. Lab. **20**, 295
96 Haupt, A. W. (1926). Bot. Gaz. **82**, 30
97 Herzfelder, H. (1921). Flora, **114**, 385
98 Herzog, T. (1926). *Geographie der Moose.* Jena
99 Herzog, T. (1942). Flora, **136**, 264
100 Herzog, T. (1952). Rev. bryol. lichen. **21**, 46
101 Höfler, K. (1946). Anz. Akad. Wiss. Wien. **3**, 5
102 Hofmeister, W. (1862). *On the germination, development and fructification of the higher Cryptogamia.* London.
103 Holferty, G. M. (1904). Bot. Gaz. **37**, 106
104 Hope-Simpson, J. F. (1941). J. Ecol. **29**, 107
105 Hooker, W. J. (1816). *British Jungermanniae.* London
106 Hörmann, H. (1959). Nova Hedwigia, **1**, 203
107 Hosokawa, T. and Kubota, H. (1957). J. Ecol. **45**, 579
108 Howe, M. A. (1899). Mem. Torrey bot. Cl. **7**, 1
109 Hy, F. (1884). Ann. Sci. nat. bot. VI. **18**, 105
110 Ikeno, S. (1903). Bot. Centralbl. **15**, 65
111 Ingold, C. T. (1939). *Spore discharge in land plants.* Oxford
112 Ingold, C. T. (1959). Trans. bot. Soc. Edinb. **38**, 76
113 Irmscher, E. (1912). Jb. wiss. Bot. **50**, 387
114 Iwatsuki, Z. (1960). J. Hattori bot. Lab. **22**, 159
115 Jack, J. B. (1895). Flora, **81**, 1
116 Joensson, B. and Olin, E. (1898). Lunds Univ. Arsskr. **34**, 440
117 Johnson, D. S. (1904). Bot. Gaz. **38**, 85
118 Jones, E. W. (1952–3). Trans. Brit. bryol. Soc. **2**, 19 and 220
119 Jones, E. W. (1958). Trans. Brit. bryol. Soc. **3**, 353
120 Jones, E. W. (1962). Trans. Brit. bryol. Soc. **4**, 254
121 Kachroo, P. (1955). J. Hattori bot. Lab. **15**, 70
122 Kamerling, Z. (1898). Flora, **85**, 157

123   Kashyap, S. R. and Dutt, N. L. (1925). Proc. Lahore phil. Soc. **4**, 49
124   Koch, L. F. (1956). Bryologist, **59**, 23
125   Kofler, L. (1959). Rev. bryol. lichen. **28**, 1
126   Kraemer, H. (1901). Bot. Gaz. **32**, 422
127   Kreh, W. (1909). Nova Acta Leop.—Carol. Akad. **90**, 89 pp.
128   Landwehr, J. (1951). Buxbaumia, **5**, 26
129   Lang, W. H. (1907). Ann. Bot. **21**, 201
130   Lange, O. L. (1955). Flora, **142**, 381
131   Leach, W. (1930). J. Ecol. **18**, 324
132   Leitgeb, H. (1875). *Untersuchungen über die Lebermoose*, Heft 2. Die Foliosen Jungermannieen. Jena
133   Leitgeb, H. (1879). *Untersuchungen über die Lebermoose*, Heft 5. Die Anthoceroteen. Graz
134   Leitgeb, H. (1881). *Die Marchantiaceen und allgemeine Bemerkungen über Lebermoose*. Graz
135   Lewis, K. R. (1961). Trans. Brit. bryol. Soc. **4**, 111
136   Lodge, E. (1959). J. Linn. Soc. Lond. **56**, 218
137   Longton, R. E. (1962). Trans. Brit. bryol. Soc. **4**, 326
138   Lorch, W. (1931). Anatomie der Laubmoose. In Linsbauer, K., *Handbuch der Pflanzenanatomie*, Bd. VII. Berlin
139   Lotsy, J. P. (1909). *Vorträge über botanische Stammesgeschichte*. Jena
140   Lowry, R. J. (1948). Mem. Torrey bot. Cl. **20**, 1
141   Lowry, R. J. (1954). Bryologist, **57**, 1
142   Lundblad, B. (1954). Svensk bot. Tidskr. **48**, 381
143   MacQuarrie, G. and Maltzahn, K. E. v. (1959). Canad. J. Bot. **37**, 121
144   Macvicar, S. M. (1926). *The student's handbook of British hepatics*. London, 464 pp.
145   Mägdefrau, K. (1935). Z. Bot. **29**, 337
146   Mahabele, T. S. (1942). Proc. Indian Acad. Sci. Ser. B, **16**, 141
147   Malta, N. (1921). Acta Univ. Latviensis. **1**, 125
148   Manton, I. (1957). J. exper. Bot. **8**, 382
149   Manton, I. and Clarke, B. (1952). J. exper. Bot. **3**, 265
150   Martin, W. (1951). Trans. Brit. bryol. Soc. **1**, 471
151   Mehra, P. N. (1957). Amer. J. Bot. **44**, 505 and 573
152   Mehra, P. N. and Kachroo, P. (1951). Bryologist, **54**, 1
153   Menge, F. (1930). Flora, **124**, 423
154   Meusel, H. (1935). Nota Acta Leopold. N.F., **3**, 123
155   Mirimanoff-Olivet, A. (1943). Ber. Schweiz. bot. Ges. **53**, 389
156   Mitra, G. C. and Allsopp, A. (1959). Nature (Lond.), **183**, 974
157   Mitra, G. C., Allsopp, A. and Wareing, P. F. (1959). Phytomorphology, **9**, 47
158   Muggoch, H. and Walton, J. (1942). Proc. roy. Soc. B, **130**, 448
159   Müller, K. (1954). Die Lebermoose Europas. Rabenhorst's *Kryptogamen-Flora*. Bd. 6, 1. 756 pp. Leipzig
160   Neuburg, M. F. (1956). C. R. Acad. Sci. U.S.S.R. **107**, 2
161   Neuburg, M. F. (1958). J. palaeontolog. Soc. Ind. (Sahn Mem. no.) **3**, 23
162   Neuburg, M. F. (1960). Akad. Nauk. U.S.S.R. **19**, 104 pp.
163   Newton, L. (1954). Famous plants. 5. Fucus. New Biology. **17**, 96

164   Noguchi, A. (1948–51). J. Hattori Bot. Lab. **3**, 53; **4**, 1; **5**, 7
165   Noguchi, A. and Osada, T. (1960). J. Hattori Bot. Lab. **23**, 122
166   Nyholm, E. (1954–60). Moss Flora of Fennoscandia II. Musci.
       Fasc. 1–4. Lund
167   Ochi, H. (1957). Jap. J. Ecol. **7**, 51
168   Ochi, H. (1959). Biolog. Inst. Tottori. 124 pp.
169   O'Hanlon, Sr. M. E. (1926). Bot. Gaz. **82**, 215
170   Pagan, F. M. (1932). Bot. Gaz. **93**, 71
171   Pandé, S. K. (1932). J. Indian bot. Soc. **11**, 169
172   Pandé, S. K. (1934). Proc. Indian Acad, Sci. B. **5**, 205
173   Parihar, N. S. (1959). *An introduction to Embryophyta*. Vol. 1,
       Bryophyta. Allahabad. (New, 4th Edn. 1961)
174   Paton, J. A. (1954). Trans. Brit. bryol. Soc. **2**, 349
175   Paton, J. A. (1956). Trans. Brit. bryol. Soc. **3**, 103
176   Paton, J. A. (1961). Trans. Brit. bryol. Soc. 4, 1
177   Paton, J. A. and Goodman, P. J. (1955). Trans. Brit. bryol. Soc. **2**,
       561
178   Paton, J. A. and Pearce, J. V. (1957). Trans. Brit. bryol. Soc. **3**, 228
179   Peirce, G. J. (1906). Bot. Gaz. **42**, 55
180   Perring, F. (1959). J. Ecol. **47**, 447
181   Perring, F. (1960). J. Ecol. **48**, 415
182   Perry, A. R. and Warburg, E. F. (1962). Trans. Brit. bryol. Soc. **4**,
       335
183   Persson, H. (1956). J. Hattori bot. Lab. **17**, 1
184   Philibert, H. (1884). Rev. bryol. **11**, 49 (et al.)
185   Proctor, M. C. F. (1956). Trans. Brit. bryol. Soc. **3**, 1
186   Proskauer, J. (1948). Ann. Bot. N.S. **12**, 237 and 427
187   Proskauer, J. (1951). Bryologist, **54**, 243
188   Proskauer, J. (1954). J. Linn. Soc. Bot. **55**, 143
188a   Proskauer, J. (1960). Phytomorphology, **10**, 1
189   Rancken, H. (1914). Acta Soc. Fauna Flora fenn. **39**, no. 2. (Dis-
       sertation)
190   Ratcliffe, D. A. and Walker, D. (1958). J. Ecol. **46**, 407
191   Reimers, H. (1954). Bryophyta; in Engler, *Syllabus der Pflanzen-
       familien*, 218–68
192   Reissinger, A. (1950). Palaeontographica, **90B**, 99
193   Richards, P. W. (1929). J. Ecol. **17**, 127
194   Richards, P. W. (1932). Ecology. In Verdoorn, F. *Manual of Bryo-
       logy*, 367
195   Richards, P. W. (1947). Trans. Brit. bryol. Soc. **1**, 1
196   Richards, P. W. (1959). Bryophyta. In *Vistas of botany* (ed. W. B.
       Turrill), 387
197   Richards, P. W. and Wallace, E. C. (1950). Trans. Brit. bryol.
       Soc. **1**, 427
198   Romell, L. G. (1939). Svensk bot. Tidskr. **33**, 366
199   Rose, F. (1949–51). Trans. Brit. bryol. Soc. **1**, 202, 255 and 427
200   Rose, F. (1953). Proc. Linn. Soc. Lond. **164**, 186
201   Ruhland, W. (1924). Musci. Allgemeiner Teil. In Engler and Prantl,
       Die natürlichen Pflanzenfamilien. Bd. 10, Leipzig.
202   Sainsbury, G. O. K. (1955). *A handbook of the New Zealand mosses*.
       Wellington, N.Z.

203 Sato, S. (1956). Bot. Mag. Tokyo, **69**, 435
204 Savicz-Ljubitzkaja, L. I. and Abramov, I. I. (1959). Rev. bryol. lichen. **28**, 330
205 Schiffner, V. (1893). Hepaticae. In Engler and Prantl, *Die natürlichen Pflanzenfamilien.* 1 Th. 3 Abt.
206 Schiffner, V. (1913). Öst. bot. Z. 63
207 Schostakowitsch, W. (1894). Flora, **79**, 350
208 Schuster, R. M. (1951). Amer. Midl. Nat. **45**, 1
209 Schuster, R. M. (1962). Trans. Brit. bryol. Soc. **4**, 230
210 Schuster, R. M. and Hattori, S. (1954). J. Hattori bot. Lab. **11**, 11
211 Scott, D. H. (rev. by C. T. Ingold, 1955). *Introduction to structural botany I.* Flowerless plants. London.
212 Shacklette, H. T. (1961). Bryologist, **64**, 1
213 Showalter, A. M. (1926). Ann. Bot. **40**, 691
214 Showalter, A. M. (1928). Cellule, **38**, 295
215 Sinoir, Y. (1952). Rev. bryol. lichen. **21**, 32
216 Sironval, C. (1947). Bull. Soc. bot. Belg. **79**, 48
217 Skene, M. (1915). Ann, Bot. **29**, 65
218 Smith, G. M. (1955). *Cryptogamic botany,* vol. 2. London (2nd ed.)
219 Sowter, F. A. (1948). Trans. Brit. bryol. Soc. **1**, 73
220 Spruce, R. (1884). Trans. bot. Soc. Edinb. **15.** 1
221 Steere, W. C. (1947). Bryologist, **50**, 247
222 Steere, W. C. (1954). Bot. Gaz. **116**, 93
223 Strunk, R. (1914). *Beiträge zur Kenntnis der Organisation der Moose.* Dissert., Bonn.
224 Swinscow, T. D. V. (1959). Trans. Brit. bryol. Soc. **3**, 509
225 Tallis, J. H. (1958–9). J. Ecol. **46**, 271; **47**, 325
226 Tamm, C. O. (1953). Medd. Skogsforskn.-Inst. Stockholm, **43.** 140 pp.
227 Tansley, A. G. (1939). *The British Islands and their vegetation.* Cambridge
228 Tansley, A. G. and Chick, E. (1901). Ann. Bot. **15**, 1
229 Tatuno, S. (1955). J. Hattori bot. Lab. **14**, 109
230 Tatuno, S. (1958). J. Hattori bot. Lab. **20**, 119
231 Townrow, J. (1959). J. S. Afr. Bot. **25**, 1
232 Vaarama, A. (1956). Irish Nat. J. **12**, 30
233 van Andel, O. M. (1952). Trans. Brit. bryol. Soc. **2**, 74
234 Verdoorn, F. (1950). Bryologist, **53**, 1
235 Vöchting, H. (1886). Jb. wiss. Bot. **16**, 367
236 Walker, R. and Pennington, W. (1939). New Phytol. **38**, 62
237 Wallace, E. C. (1950). Trans. Brit. bryol. Soc. **1**, 327
238 Walton, J. (1925). Ann. Bot. **39**, 563
239 Walton, J. (1928). Ann. Bot. **42**, 707
240 Walton, J. (1943). Nature (Lond.), **152**, 51
241 Warburg, E. F. (1949). Trans. Brit. bryol. Soc. **1**, 199
242 Watson, E. V. (1950). Trans. Brit. bryol. Soc. **1**, 345
243 Watson, E. V. (1953). Trans. bot. Soc. Edinb. **36**, 165
244 Watson, E. V. (1955). *British mosses and liverworts.* Cambridge, 419 pp.
245 Watson, E. V. (1957). Famous plants. 6. Funaria. New Biology **22**, 104
246 Watson, E. V. (1960). J. Ecol. **48**, 397

247 Watson, E. V. (1960). Trans. bot. Soc. Edinb. **39**, 85
248 Watson, H. (1947). *Woodland mosses*. Forestry Commission book-
     let, no. 1. London, H.M. Stationery Office
249 Watson, W. (1913). New Phytol. **13**, 149
250 Watson, W. (1918). J. Ecol. **6**, 126 and 189
251 Watson, W. (1925). J. Ecol. **13**, 22
252 Watson, W. (1932). J. Ecol. **20**, 284
253 Watt, A. S. and Jones, E. W. (1948). J. Ecol. **36**, 283
254 Wettstein, F. von (1923). Biol. Zbl. **43**, 71
255 Wettstein, F. von (1924). Z. indukt. Abstamm. Vererbl. **33**, 1
256 Wettstein, F. von (1940). Ber. dtsch. bot. Ges. **58**, 374
257 Wettstein, F. von and Straub, J. (1942). Z. indukt. Abstamm.
     Vererbl. **80**, 271
258 Wettstein, R. (1924). *Handbuch der systematischen Botanik*. Aufl.
     3, Leipzig
259 Whitehouse, H. L. K. (1961). Trans. Brit. bryol. Soc. **4**, 84
260 Wigglesworth, G. (1947). Trans. Brit. bryol. Soc. **1**, 4
261 Williams, S. (1950). Trans. Brit. bryol. Soc. **1**, 357
262 Wilson, M. (1911). Ann. Bot. 25, 415
263 Wylie, A. P. (1957). Trans. Brit. bryol. Soc. **3**, 260
264 Yano, K. (1956). Bot. Mag. Tokyo, **69**, 156
265 Yano, K. (1957). Mem. Fac. Ed. Niigata Univ. 6, no. **3**, 1
266 Zacherl, H. (1956). Z. Bot. **44**, 409
267 Zielinski, F. (1910). Flora, **100**, 1

Index

Page numbers in heavy type refer to illustrations